FORTRAN FOR PHYSICS

FORTRAN FOR PHYSICS

ALFRED M. BORK

REED COLLEGE

ADDISON-WESLEY PUBLISHING COMPANY

READING, MASSACHUSETTS • PALO ALTO • LONDON • DON MILLS, ONTARIO

This book is in the **Addison-Wesley Series in Physics**

PREFACE

This book is a self-contained text on computers in elementary physics which employs classical mechanics as its base; it attempts to provide an understanding of computer programming in relation to an understanding of physics. Designed to complement both beginning physics and physical science courses, it may be used by science majors and nonscience majors as well. The serious high school student will find it readable, and the advanced student of physics who has not had previous experience with computer techniques and languages may find it useful.

Computer techniques deserve a place in the subject matter of the elementary physics course for several definite reasons: First, the close association between the computer field and the fields of science and engineering is well known. If a student is eventually to concentrate in one of these fields, the earlier he masters fundamental computer techniques the better; indeed, this understanding will prove to be a basic tool for him in all the areas of science. Because of the emerging importance of the computer in the sciences, educators ought to determine the most convenient and reasonable ways for science majors to learn programming. In my opinion there is a marked advantage in introducing the student to the computer in a situation in which there is a real need and use for it, rather than in a general programming course. Because applications are at hand, the theory and fundamental techniques can be displayed in working conditions and thereby made more intelligible to the student.

A second reason for including this supplementary material in an elementary course is that it allows the course to exploit for teaching purposes the excitement that computers continue to generate. Most students entering colleges and universities today have read about computers fairly extensively in the press, at least, and to most of them the computer seems an almost magical device. It is easy and profitable to capitalize on students' enthusiasm about the use of these machines.

Furthermore, the employment of computers in a physics or physical science course for nonscience majors introduces these students to a device which is playing a

v

vital and enormously important role in our society. At the present time, there is no customary place for the introduction of computers to the nonscientist. This text enables the instructor to use a part of the time of his course for this purpose. I believe that such a procedure provides at the same time an effective means of conveying the central material of the course.

Finally, and very importantly, the typical elementary course makes no use of differential equations because it cannot usually be assumed that a student's mathematical background is broad enough to include familiarity with them. Differential equations can be approached from the point of view of either analytical solution or numerical solution. Students without an analytical background readily understand numerical solutions. The computations involved may be cumbersome, however; and while numerical methods allow the students to understand the use of differential equations at an early stage, it is computer programming that makes early introduction of them a practical instructional innovation, since by the numerical methods used in conjunction with computer programming the student can obtain actual solutions to differential equations in a reasonable time. Furthermore, if the student learns programming early in the course of study, numerical techniques can be used more extensively at the intermediate and advanced levels.

The programming language used in this book is FORTRAN, by far the most common algebraic programming language in current use. FORTRAN is not entirely ideal for teaching purposes, particularly in comparison with some of the new algebraic languages, but it is satisfactory. The general approach to FORTRAN here, in contrast to that taken in the usual manuals, is not grammatical. The text does not begin with a careful grammatical discussion of the elements of FORTRAN but rather presents the language through a series of sample programs involving calculations already familiar to the student. Thus it teaches FORTRAN in the way a child is taught his native language, through use rather than through study of grammar and vocabulary.

Because FORTRAN is not a single language, but a language with almost as many dialects as there are individual computer installations, a decision had to be made as to which dialect of FORTRAN to use. In the examples, I have chosen to use the FORTRAN II-D language for the IBM 1620 with disk file. As most of the details of the discussions are independent of particular machines or compilers, this should not be a serious disadvantage. References made to a particular computer usually are to the IBM 1620, a small computer already installed in many schools and one which may be increasingly available for instructional use as it is replaced for research purposes by newer and faster machines. However, dependence on the 1620 is weak, as can be seen by a quick look through the material, and the book should be useful with different systems.

I have assumed that the student will use this book as a general introduction to FORTRAN. If a student continues with programming, he will presumably have access to the FORTRAN manual of his computing center and will be able to consult this manual on details of the system in use there. It would have been possible to give detailed material in appendices on various versions of FORTRAN, but this did not seem very desirable. Not only is there so much variation between FORTRAN dialects that the appendices could be of only limited value to begin with, but such information would rapidly become outdated and useless. The general comments on FORTRAN in the text attempt to take into account some of the newer versions of the language.

Problems have been spaced strategically throughout the text rather than grouped at the ends of the chapters. Most of the problems are demanding.

I believe that this book can be used with or without an available computer. It will contribute something to a course in physics even if it is not possible to run problems on a computer. But I think that its pedagogical uses will be considerably enhanced if the instructor has access to the computer facility of his own school. How much access, and how many of the problems should be run, is a matter of individual choice. One could use the computer, if desired, to do much of the grading of problems.

If the center has a small computer it may be possible to have the students work in the computer room and (in a short time) run their own programs. However, only a few students can use the computer at any one time, and it may be necessary to divide the class into groups and assign off-computer tasks for part of the class. The teacher who works from a batch-processing computer center with a single program being run at one time will quickly encounter certain practical disadvantages. In a larger center it may be difficult to persuade the director of the center that the students should spend large amounts of time in the computer room, although for some of the problems this would be desirable. The particular arrangement must be worked out with the director of the center. If a time-sharing facility is available, it would make the use of the computer suggested here much more effective; however, very few instructors are fortunate enough to have such a system available, and the language of such a system is not likely to be FORTRAN.

The question of how much material will be used in the course is a matter of decision for the individual teacher. After trying several arrangements, in my classes I have decided to use the laboratory time for the computer material. In the course given from the notes which led to this book, I used classroom time only for the three-body problem. Thus all the earlier introduction to FORTRAN occurred entirely within the laboratories. (I am not suggesting that the computer replace entirely the conventional laboratory.) I used a block of laboratory time, but it might be convenient to alternate computer laboratories with conventional laboratories. The advantage of laboratory time is the long uninterrupted period, within which difficulties can be discovered and overcome. However, some instructors might feel unhappy about taking time from conventional laboratory uses.

I want to express a debt of gratitude to the students in my classes for nonscience majors at Reed College during the past three years. The interactive nature of the Reed student body, and the high level of ability of the students who choose to come to Reed, have made it a pleasure to teach this course. I should also like to thank several colleagues in physics at Reed who have a particular interest in using computers in teaching physics at various levels: John Shonle, Dennis Hoffman, and Robert Reynolds. My wife Annette read sections of the manuscript and suggested many useful stylistic improvements.

Portland, Oregon
January 1967

A. M. B.

CONTENTS

CHAPTER 1

THE DIGITAL COMPUTER

Students become acquainted with computers and computer programming in many ways. The methods encountered often take little account of the background or interests of the students; however, it would appear that there are interesting opportunities for physics students to become familiar with computers through the study of physical problems.

The area of physics concerning us is classical mechanics, the study of the motion of bodies. The specific treatment of mechanics we shall use comes from the *Feynman Lectures on Physics*, Volume I, Chapter 9, which is reprinted as the second chapter of this book. Before considering Feynman's treatment of mechanics, however, we briefly examine the structure of a modern digital computer.

Numerical calculations are very useful in many different areas of science. But experience with such calculations quickly shows that they often involve a large amount of work, mostly sheer arithmetical labor consisting of addition, subtraction, multiplication, and division. Furthermore, the work is boring, being a rote process that requires no active intelligence. One could instruct an "assistant" or "clerk" to carry out the necessary operations for a particular problem, without bothering to teach him the details of the area of science needed to formulate the problem. It is easy to see what the job requirements for such an assistant are.

1 He must be able to type or write in order to record the necessary information.

2 He must be able to add, subtract, multiply, and divide—i.e., he must be able to carry out the numerical operations which are the basis for all calculation.

3 He must be able to compare two numbers and decide which is greater. For example, such a comparison may be necessary to decide when the problem is finished.

4 He must be able to follow a sequential, step-by-step set of instructions without constant outside aid, doing one instruction after another.

5 He must be able to "remember" numbers to use in a later stage of the calculation. This might involve writing them down in an orderly fashion.

Few of you will be surprised to hear that these tasks are not so demanding as to require performance by a human being—they can be carried out by specialized electromechanical devices, computers. Such machines have been developed only recently, the first having been built at the end of the Second World War, but the idea is an old one.

Machines have been able to perform certain of these functions for many years—slide rules and desk calculators can carry out some or all of the arithmetical operations mentioned in **2.** The greatest problem was to develop a machine able to carry out **4,** the storing and executing of instructions; such a machine must "absorb" the entire set of instructions before it begins to carry any of them to completion. If we were to point to an individual who saw the value of, and who showed how to develop, such "stored program" machines, it would be the mathematician, John von Neumann. The modern digital computer is a descendant of his conceptions.

The reader may not realize how new the computer is, but he is likely to know that it already has made considerable impact on our society. At the moment perhaps 30,000 digital computers are used in a very wide variety of situations in the United States, probably at an average cost of about $250,000 per computer. Almost all of them have been built since about 1958, when reliable production models were first available. The major technical revolution in computer technology was the change from vacuum tubes to transistors, and recently the use of "integrated" circuitry, which permits the production of previously separate components as a single small circuit, has also been important. Almost no area of technology is developing as rapidly as computer technology.

In spite of the influence that the computer has had, it is easy to underestimate its future possibilities. The computer has been consistently underestimated—even computer manufacturers have underestimated the number of computers that could be sold. Many future applications will differ greatly from the numerical applications which are our concern here.

THE DIGITAL COMPUTER; ITS PARTS

There is no simple way of describing computers. We shall list the basic "pieces" of the digital computer, describing briefly the function of each component, but not considering electronic construction details.

We begin with the memory of the computer. Memory is an anthropomorphic term, a word commonly used to describe people rather than machines. Many terms describing computers have this property. The memory of a computer stores numbers, or more accurately, coded symbols of any kind. Physically, memories are built in different ways. The most common fast memories are magnetic core memories, tiny doughnuts of magnetic material; in almost all computers today the main memory is a magnetic core memory. Other memory systems in common use are magnetic tapes and magnetic disks or drums which often serve as secondary storage for very large quantities of information. These devices have a common property: the magnetic core can be magnetized in either of two ways, "way" referring to the direction of its north pole, and similar considerations hold for tapes, drums, and disks. Thus, internally, computers do not use 0, 1, 2, 3, 4, 5, 6, 7, 8, 9, but only 0 and 1. Mathematicians have known the concept of the binary or base-two number for centuries, but only recently did Norbert Wiener and others suggest that these numbers were desirable for computer manipulation. For numbers to be used in computers, the individual number is presented in binary form, or each digit of the numbers is separately represented as a binary number, or the number is coded with zeros and ones. This process differs from computer to computer. But the input and output of computers are not restricted to binary numbers, so the user may encounter only the well-known decimal or base-ten numbers. Base-eight and base-sixteen numbers are also used in some computers.

Various memory units differ widely in speed, that is, in how fast they can find what is stored. In good magnetic core memories in current use a number can be found in memory and retrieved for use in a calculation in about one-millionth of a second. Secondary (noncore) storage is slower, usually because it depends on mechanical elements as well as on purely electronic components; for example, the reading arm must move to the right place on the disk. Every number in memory is identified by an address, just as the houses on your street are identified. The quantity of numbers stored may vary greatly, running from thousands of numbers in one installation to billions in another.

Although we have discussed primarily the storage of numbers, symbols that we do not regard as numbers can also be stored in computer memories. The most obvious example is the letters of the alphabet—almost all computers store linguistic (alphabetical) as well as numerical information. In general, any symbol—numerical, alphabetical, or special—can be coded for machine storage, so the computer need not be considered to be merely a "number" machine.

In addition to the memory unit, computers have another important electronic unit which does simple arithmetic operations and compares entities in the machine's memory. The electronic circuits that perform arithmetic are based on the rules of simple logic. Addition in today's fast machines takes about one-millionth of a second, and multiplication takes slightly longer. Smaller machines may have only an "adder," but a large computer can have many arithmetical units, perhaps in several central processors. When the computer adds, it can store the sum in memory, and it can also move numbers from one address to another within the memory when called upon to do so.

A third set of components gets information, numerical or verbal, in and out of the machine. There are many different devices for this operation, and these often occupy much of the physical space devoted to the computer. A common input device is a card reader which reads the familiar punched card at a rate of about 200 to 500 80-column cards per minute. A typical output device is the line printer which prints whole lines at a time at rates that can exceed 1000 lines per minute. Thus a digital computer can generate enormous amounts of paper output in a day. A typewriter is another common input-output device, used particularly for small quantities of information. Other output machines possible are card punches, page printers, plotters, and cathode-ray tubes (with and without associated cameras).

One interesting development is that input-output devices need not be physically near the computer. Cables or telephone lines can connect remote terminals to the computer, or allow direct transfer of information by two computers in two different places, that is, the machines can "talk" to each other without a human intermediary. This decentralizing of the use stations of the computer is very likely to alter the standard ways of using the computer in the near future. Telephone companies have estimated that they will soon gain more revenue from computer data lines than from ordinary telephone lines!

So far we have described nothing more elaborate than an extremely fast and elaborate electronic adding machine. Our computer can store many more numbers much faster than a desk adding machine, and can do addition much faster, but it is not essentially different from a desk adding machine, and can do addition much faster, but it is not essentially different from a desk calculator. If we were to use it in the same manner in which we use the latter, it would not offer any significant advantage; most of the time would be spent waiting for the human operator to type the next information and to push the appropriate button. To exploit effectively the very fast storage and arithmetic speed of the modern computer we need the concept of the stored program. The instructions for an entire problem are given to the machine and stored in the memory; then the machine executes these instructions one after another. The computer obtains one instruction from the memory, does what the instruction tells it to do, and then gets the next instruction. It is this idea of the storing and using its own stored program that allows the tremendous speed of the computer, since the instructions are executed at electronic speeds.

The set of directions, critical to the whole operation, is called the program. A program can modify itself; one of the instructions in the program may change part of the program. Or, as with "reentrant" programs intended to be used by many people, it may not alter itself. Portions of a program may be used repeatedly in the same calculation. This feature allows us to work with a relatively short program which, however, will carry out mathematical procedures that fill a large block of computer time. The programmer may write only a few hundred instructions, but the computer calculation may involve the carrying out of tens or hundreds of thousands of instructions.

Corresponding to the program is another physical component of the computer, the control unit. This electronic unit takes each instruction from memory, interprets the instruction, sends out signals leading to its being carried out, and then continues with the next instruction. A typical instruction might tell the computer to find a number stored at an address in memory, add it to a number stored in another location, and then store the result at a new address. In some machines these operations might require two or three separate instructions, since the instruction code differs from machine to machine.

COMPUTERS AND LANGUAGE; FORTRAN

Our approach to this problem is one of language. But unlike English or classical mechanics, which are languages for communication between people, the languages we discuss are intended for *people-machine* communication. The situation involves giving directions—you have a problem which can be solved by some routine procedure (an *algorithm*), and you want to tell the machine how to make the necessary calculations. The process is called *programming*, and our present concern is with programming languages. Note the plural, implying that there are many such languages.

One way to learn a language is to begin by studying its grammatical structure and vocabulary. Many elementary courses in programming take this structural, or grammatical, approach. But there is another common way; suppose, for example, you were to learn French by living in France. Then you would daily encounter examples of the language and you would learn it through these particular examples. Presumably this resembles the way most people learn a language as small children.

Both of these methods can be used for computer languages. The first approach is most common, but here we shall employ the second. Our tack will be to present programs in a computer language before we have discussed that language at all and then to go through these programs, showing what each of the "sentences" does.

The language we shall be concerned with is FORTRAN (FORmula TRANslation), which was first made available about 1957. We shall later glance at its history and see that FORTRAN is not a single language, but a related family of languages. First, however, we want to fix the context in which we shall work, classical mechanics. We do this in Chapter 2 by presenting a chapter on mechanics from a beautiful introductory college physics text, the *Feynman Lectures on Physics*.

CHAPTER 2

NEWTON'S LAWS OF DYNAMICS

Reprinted with permission from
R. D. Feynman, R. B. Leighton, and M. Sands, *The Feynman Lectures on Physics*
(Reading, Mass.: Addison-Wesley, 1963) Vol. I, Chapter 9.

9-1 Momentum and force

The discovery of the laws of dynamics, or the laws of motion, was a dramatic moment in the history of science. Before Newton's time, the motions of things like the planets were a mystery, but after Newton there was complete understanding. Even the slight deviations from Kepler's laws, due to the perturbations of the planets, were computable. The motions of pendulums, oscillators with springs and weights in them, and so on, could all be analyzed completely after Newton's laws were enunciated. So it is with this chapter: before this chapter we could not calculate how a mass on a spring would move; much less could we calculate the perturbations on the planet Uranus due to Jupiter and Saturn. After this chapter we *will* be able to compute not only the motion of the oscillating mass, but also the perturbations on the planet Uranus produced by Jupiter and Saturn!

Galileo made a great advance in the understanding of motion when he discovered the *principle of inertia:* if an object is left alone, is not disturbed, it continues to move with a constant velocity in a straight line if it was originally moving, or it continues to stand still if it was just standing still. Of course this never appears to be the case in nature, for if we slide a block across a table it stops, but that is because it is *not* left to itself—it is rubbing against the table. It required a certain imagination to find the right rule, and that imagination was supplied by Galileo.

Of course, the next thing which is needed is a rule for finding how an object *changes* its speed if something *is* affecting it. That is the contribution of Newton. Newton wrote down three laws: The First Law was a mere restatement of the Galilean principle of inertia just described. The Second Law gave a specific way of determining how the velocity changes under different influences called *forces*. The Third Law describes the forces to some extent, and we shall discuss that at another time. Here we shall discuss only the Second Law, which asserts that the motion of an object is changed by forces in this way: *the time-rate-of-change of a quantity called momentum is proportional to the force.* We shall state this mathematically shortly, but let us first explain the idea.

Momentum is not the same as *velocity*. A lot of words are used in physics, and they all have precise meanings in physics, although they may not have such precise meanings in everyday language. Momentum is an example, and we must define it precisely. If we exert a certain push with our arms on an object that is light, it moves easily; if we push just as hard on another object that is much heavier in the usual sense, then it moves much less rapidly. Actually, we must change the words from "light" and "heavy" to *less massive* and *more massive*, because there is a difference to be understood between the *weight* of an object and its *inertia*. (How hard it is to get it going is one thing, and how much it weighs is something else.) Weight and inertia are *proportional*, and on the earth's surface are often taken to be numerically equal, which causes a certain confusion to the student. On Mars, weights would be different but the amount of force needed to overcome inertia would be the same.

We use the term *mass* as a quantitative measure of inertia, and we may measure mass, for example, by swinging an object in a circle at a certain speed and measuring how much force we need to keep it in the circle. In this way we find a certain quantity of mass for every object. Now the *momentum* of an object is a product of two parts: its *mass* and its *velocity*. Thus Newton's Second Law may be written mathematically this way:

$$F = \frac{d}{dt}(mv). \qquad (9.1)$$

Now there are several points to be considered. In writing down any law such as this, we use many intuitive ideas, implications, and assumptions which are at first combined approximately into our "law." Later we may have to come back and study in greater detail exactly what each term means, but if we try to do this too soon we shall get confused. Thus at the beginning we take several things for granted. First, that the mass of an object is *constant*; it isn't really, but we shall start out with the Newtonian approximation that mass is constant, the same all the time, and that, further, when we put two objects together, their masses *add*. These ideas were of course implied by Newton when he wrote his equation, for otherwise it is meaningless. For example, suppose the mass varied inversely as the velocity; then the momentum would *never change* in any circumstance, so the law means nothing unless you know how the mass changes with velocity. At first we say, *it does not change.*

Then there are some implications concerning force. As a rough approximation we think of force as a kind of push or pull that we make with our muscles, but we can define it more accurately now that we have this law of motion. The most important thing to realize is that this relationship involves not only changes in the *magnitude* of the momentum or of the velocity but also in their *direction*.

If the mass is constant, then Eq. (9.1) can also be written as

$$F = m\frac{dv}{dt} = ma. \tag{9.2}$$

The acceleration a is the rate of change of the velocity, and Newton's Second Law says more than that the effect of a given force varies inversely as the mass; it says also that the *direction* of the change in the velocity and the *direction* of the force are the same. Thus we must understand that a change in a velocity, or an acceleration, has a wider meaning than in common language: The velocity of a moving object can change by its speeding up, slowing down (when it slows down, we say it accelerates with a negative acceleration), or changing its direction of motion. An acceleration at right angles to the velocity was discussed in Chapter 7. There we saw that an object moving in a circle of radius R with a certain speed v along the circle falls away from a straightline path by a distance equal to $\frac{1}{2}(v^2/R)t^2$ if t is very small. Thus the formula for acceleration at right angles to the motion is

$$a = v^2/R, \tag{9.3}$$

and a force at right angles to the velocity will cause an object to move in a curved path whose radius of curvature can be found by dividing the force by the mass to get the acceleration, and then using (9.3).

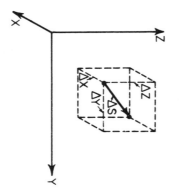

Fig. 9–1.   A small displacement of an object.

9-2 Speed and velocity

In order to make our language more precise, we shall make one further definition in our use of the words *speed* and *velocity*. Ordinarily we think of speed and velocity as being the same, and in ordinary language they are the same. But in physics we have taken advantage of the fact that there *are* two words and have chosen to use them to distinguish two ideas. We carefully distinguish velocity, which has both magnitude and direction, from speed, which we choose to mean the magnitude of the velocity, but which does not include the direction. We can formulate this more precisely by describing how the x-, y-, and z-coordinates of an object change with time. Suppose, for example, that at a certain instant an object is moving as shown in Fig. 9–1. In a given small interval of time Δt it will move a certain distance Δx in the x-direction, Δy in the y-direction, and Δz in the z-direction. The total effect of these three coordinate changes is a displacement Δs along the diagonal of a parallelepiped whose sides are Δx, Δy, and Δz. In terms of the velocity, the displacement Δx is the x-component of the velocity times Δt, and similarly for Δy and Δz:

$$\Delta x = v_x \, \Delta t, \qquad \Delta y = v_y \, \Delta t, \qquad \Delta z = v_z \, \Delta t. \qquad (9.4)$$

9-3 Components of velocity, acceleration, and force

In Eq. (9.4) *we have resolved the velocity into components* by telling how fast the object is moving in the x-direction, the y-direction, and the z-direction. The velocity is completely specified, both as to magnitude and direction, if we give the numerical values of its three rectangular components:

$$v_x = dx/dt, \qquad v_y = dy/dt, \qquad v_z = dz/dt. \qquad (9.5)$$

On the other hand, the speed of the object is

$$ds/dt = |v| = \sqrt{v_x^2 + v_y^2 + v_z^2}. \qquad (9.6)$$

Next, suppose that, because of the action of a force, the velocity changes to some other direction and a different magnitude, as shown in Fig. 9–2. We can analyze this apparently complex situation rather simply if we evaluate the changes in the x-, y-, and z-components of velocity. The change in the component of the velocity in the x-direction in a time Δt is $\Delta v_x = a_x \, \Delta t$, where a_x is what we call the x-component of the acceleration. Similarly, we see that $\Delta v_y = a_y \, \Delta t$ and $\Delta v_z = a_z \, \Delta t$. In these terms, we see that Newton's Second Law, in saying that the force is in the same direction as the acceleration, is really three laws, in the sense that the component of the force in the x-, y-, or z-direction is equal to the mass times

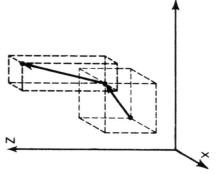

Fig. 9–2. A change in velocity in which both the magnitude and direction change.

the rate of change of the corresponding component of velocity:

$$F_x = m(dv_x/dt) = m(d^2x/dt^2) = ma_x,$$
$$F_y = m(dv_y/dt) = m(d^2y/dt^2) = ma_y,$$
$$F_z = m(dv_z/dt) = m(d^2z/dt^2) = ma_z.$$

(9.7)

Just as the velocity and acceleration have been resolved into components by projecting a line segment representing the quantity and its direction onto three coordinate axes, so, in the same way, a force in a given direction is represented by certain components in the x-, y-, and z-directions:

$$F_x = F\cos(x, F),$$
$$F_y = F\cos(y, F),$$
$$F_z = F\cos(z, F),$$

(9.8)

where F is the magnitude of the force and (x, F) represents the angle between the x-axis and the direction of F, etc.

Newton's Second Law is given in complete form in Eq. (9.7). If we know the forces on an object and resolve them into x-, y-, and z-components, then we can find the motion of the object from these equations. Let us consider a simple example. Suppose there are no forces in the y- and z-directions, the only force being in the x-direction, say vertically. Equation (9.7) tells us that there would be changes in the velocity in the vertical direction, but no changes in the horizontal direction. This was demonstrated with a special apparatus in Chapter 7 (see Fig. 7–3). A falling body moves horizontally without any change in horizontal motion, while it moves vertically the same way as it would move if the horizontal motion were zero. In other words, motions in the x-, y-, and z-directions are independent if the *forces* are not connected.

9–4 What is the force?

In order to use Newton's laws, we have to have some formula for the force; these laws say *pay attention to the forces*. If an object is accelerating, some agency is at work; find it. Our program for the future of dynamics must be to *find the laws for the force*. Newton himself went on to give some examples. In the case of gravity he gave a specific formula for the force. In the case of other forces he gave some part of the information in his Third Law, which we will study in the next chapter, having to do with the equality of action and reaction.

Extending our previous example, what are the forces on objects near the earth's surface? Near the earth's surface, the force in the vertical direction due to gravity is proportional to the mass of the object and is nearly independent of height for heights small compared with the earth's radius R: $F = GmM/R^2 = mg$, where $g = GM/R^2$ is called the *acceleration of gravity*. Thus the law of gravity tells us that weight is proportional to mass; the force is in the vertical direction and is the mass times g. Again we find that the motion in the horizontal direction

EQUILIBRIUM
POSITION
x
m

Fig. 9–3.   A mass on a spring.

is at constant velocity.   The interesting motion is in the vertical direction, and Newton's Second Law tells us

$$mg = m(d^2x/dt^2). \qquad (9.9)$$

Cancelling the m's, we find that the acceleration in the x-direction is constant and equal to g.   This is of course the well known law of free fall under gravity, which leads to the equations

$$v_x = v_0 + gt,$$
$$x = x_0 + v_0 t + \tfrac{1}{2}gt^2. \qquad (9.10)$$

As another example, let us suppose that we have been able to build a gadget (Fig. 9–3) which applies a force proportional to the distance and directed oppositely —a spring.   If we forget about gravity, which is of course balanced out by the initial stretch of the spring, and talk only about *excess* forces, we see that if we pull the mass down, the spring pulls up, while if we push it up the spring pulls down.   This machine has been designed carefully so that the force is greater, the more we pull it up, in exact proportion to the displacement from the balanced condition, and the force upward is similarly proportional to how far we pull down. If we watch the dynamics of this machine, we see a rather beautiful motion—up, down, up, down, . . .   The question is, will Newton's equations correctly describe this motion?   Let us see whether we can exactly calculate how it moves with this periodic oscillation, by applying Newton's law (9.7).   In the present instance, the equation is

$$-kx = m(dv_x/dt). \qquad (9.11)$$

Here we have a situation where the velocity in the x-direction changes at a rate proportional to x.   Nothing will be gained by retaining numerous constants, so we shall imagine either that the scale of time has changed or that there is an accident in the units, so that we happen to have $k/m = 1$.   Thus we shall try to solve the equation

$$dv_x/dt = -x. \qquad (9.12)$$

To proceed, we must know what v_x is, but of course we know that the velocity is the rate of change of the position.

9–5   Meaning of the dynamical equations

Now let us try to analyze just what Eq. (9.12) means.   Suppose that at a given time t the object has a certain velocity v_x and position x.   What is the velocity and what is the position at a slightly later time $t + \epsilon$? If we can answer this question our problem is solved, for then we can start with the given condition and compute how it changes for the first instant, the next instant, the next instant, and so on, and in this way we gradually evolve the motion. To be specific, let us suppose that at the time $t = 0$ we are given that $x = 1$ and $v_x = 0$. Why does the object move at all? Because there is a *force* on it when it is at any position except $x = 0$. If $x > 0$, that force is upward. Therefore the velocity which is zero starts to change, because of the law of motion. Once it starts to build up some velocity the object starts to move up, and so on. Now at any time t, if ϵ is very small, we may express the position at time $t + \epsilon$ in terms of the position at time t and the velocity at time t to a very good approximation as

$$x(t + \epsilon) = x(t) + \epsilon v_x(t). \qquad (9.13)$$

The smaller the ϵ, the more accurate this expression is, but it is still usefully accurate even if ϵ is not vanishingly small. Now what about the velocity? In order to get the velocity later, the velocity at the time $t + \epsilon$, we need to know how the velocity changes, the *acceleration*. And how are we going to find the acceleration? That is where the law of dynamics comes in. The law of dynamics tells us what the acceleration is. It says the acceleration is $-x$.

Equation (9.14) is merely kinematics; it says that a velocity changes because of the presence of acceleration. But Eq. (9.15) is *dynamics*, because it relates the acceleration to the force; it says that at this particular time for this particular problem, you can replace the acceleration by $-x(t)$. Therefore, if we know both the x and v at a given time, we know the acceleration, which tells us the new velocity, and we know the new position—this is how the machinery works. The velocity changes a little bit because of the force, and the position changes a little bit because of the velocity.

$$v_x(t + \epsilon) = v_x(t) + \epsilon a_x(t) \qquad (9.14)$$
$$= v_x(t) - \epsilon x(t). \qquad (9.15)$$

9–6 Numerical solution of the equations

Now let us really solve the problem. Suppose that we take $\epsilon = 0.100$ sec. After we do all the work if we find that this is not small enough we may have to go back and do it again with $\epsilon = 0.010$ sec. Starting with our initial value $x(0) = 1.00$, what is $x(0.1)$? It is the old position $x(0)$ plus the velocity (which is zero) times 0.10 sec. Thus $x(0.1)$ is still 1.00 because it has not yet started to move. But the new velocity at 0.10 sec will be the old velocity $v(0) = 0$ plus ϵ times the acceleration. The acceleration is $-x(0) = -1.00$. Thus

$$v(0.1) = 0.00 - 0.10 \times 1.00 = -0.10.$$

Now at 0.20 sec

$$x(0.2) = x(0.1) + \epsilon v(0.1)$$
$$= 1.00 - 0.10 \times 0.10 = 0.99$$

and

$$v(0.2) = v(0.1) + \epsilon a(0.1)$$
$$= -0.10 - 0.10 \times 1.00 = -0.20.$$

And so, on and on and on, we can calculate the rest of the motion, and that is just what we shall do. However, for practical purposes there are some little tricks by which we can increase the accuracy. If we continued this calculation as we have started it, we would find the motion only rather crudely because $\epsilon = 0.100$ sec is rather crude, and we would have to go to a very small interval, say $\epsilon = 0.01$. Then to go through a reasonable total time interval would take a lot of cycles of computation. So we shall organize the work in a way that will increase the precision of our calculations, using the same coarse interval $\epsilon = 0.10$ sec. This can be done if we make a subtle improvement in the technique of the analysis.

Notice that the new position is the old position plus the time interval ϵ times the velocity. But the velocity *when?* The velocity at the beginning of the time interval is one velocity and the velocity at the end of the time interval is another velocity. Our improvement is to use the velocity *halfway between.* If we know the speed now, but the speed is changing, then we are not going to get the right answer by going at the same speed as now. We should use some speed between the "now" speed and the "then" speed at the end of the interval. The same considerations also apply to the velocity: to compute the velocity changes, we should use the acceleration midway between the two times at which the velocity is to be found. Thus the equations that we shall actually use will be something like this: the position later is equal to the position before plus ϵ times the velocity *at the time in the middle of the interval.* Similarly, the velocity at this halfway point is the velocity at a time ϵ before (which is in the middle of the previous interval) plus ϵ times the acceleration at the time t. That is, we use the equations

$$x(t + \epsilon) = x(t) + \epsilon v(t + \epsilon/2),$$
$$v(t + \epsilon/2) = v(t - \epsilon/2) + \epsilon a(t), \qquad (9.16)$$
$$a(t) = -x(t).$$

There remains only one slight problem: what is $v(\epsilon/2)$? At the start, we are given $v(0)$, not $v(-\epsilon/2)$. To get our calculation started, we shall use a special equation, namely, $v(\epsilon/2) = v(0) + (\epsilon/2)a(0)$.

Now we are ready to carry through our calculation. For convenience, we may arrange the work in the form of a table, with columns for the time, the position, the velocity, and the acceleration, and the in-between lines for the velocity, as shown in Table 9–1. Such a table is, of course, just a convenient way of representing the numerical values obtained from the set of equations (9.16), and in fact the equations themselves need never be written. We just fill in the various spaces in

Table 9-1

Solution of $dv_x/dt = -x$

Interval: $\epsilon = 0.10$ sec

t	x	v_x	a_x
0.0	1.000	0.000	−1.000
		−0.050	
0.1	0.995		−0.995
		−0.150	
0.2	0.980		−0.980
		−0.248	
0.3	0.955		−0.955
		−0.343	
0.4	0.921		−0.921
		−0.435	
0.5	0.877	−0.523	−0.877
0.6	0.825	−0.605	−0.825
0.7	0.764	−0.682	−0.764
0.8	0.696	−0.751	−0.696
0.9	0.621	−0.814	−0.621
1.0	0.540	−0.868	−0.540
1.1	0.453	−0.913	−0.453
1.2	0.362	−0.949	−0.362
1.3	0.267	−0.976	−0.267
1.4	0.169	−0.993	−0.169
1.5	0.070	−1.000	−0.070
1.6	−0.030		+0.030

the table one by one. This table now gives us a very good idea of the motion: it starts from rest, first picks up a little upward (negative) velocity and it loses some of its distance. The acceleration is then a little bit less but it is still gaining speed. But as it goes on it gains speed more and more slowly, until as it passes $x = 0$ at about $t = 1.50$ sec we can confidently predict that it will keep going, but now it will be on the other side; the position x will become negative, the ac-

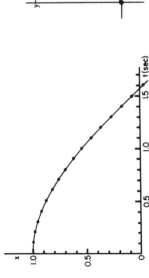

Fig. 9–4. Graph of the motion of a mass on a spring.

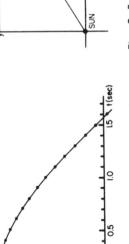

Fig. 9–5. The force of gravity on a planet.

celeration therefore positive. Thus the speed decreases. It is interesting to compare these numbers with the function $x = \cos t$, which is done in Fig. 9–4. The agreement is within the three significant figure accuracy of our calculation! We shall see later that $x = \cos t$ is the exact mathematical solution of our equation of motion, but it is an impressive illustration of the power of numerical analysis that such an easy calculation should give such precise results.

9-7 Planetary motions

The above analysis is very nice for the motion of an oscillating spring, but can we analyze the motion of a planet around the sun? Let us see whether we can arrive at an approximation to an ellipse for the orbit. We shall suppose that the sun is infinitely heavy, in the sense that we shall not include its motion. Suppose a planet starts at a certain place and is moving with a certain velocity; it goes around the sun in some curve, and we shall try to analyze, by Newton's laws of motion and his law of gravitation, what the curve is. How? At a given moment it is at some position in space. If the radial distance from the sun to this position is called r, then we know that there is a force directed inward which, according to the law of gravity, is equal to a constant times the product of the sun's mass and the planet's mass divided by the square of the distance. To analyze this further we must find out what acceleration will be produced by this force. We shall need the *components* of the acceleration along two directions, which we call x and y. Thus if we specify the position of the planet at a given moment by giving x and y (we shall suppose that z is always zero because there is no force in the z-direction and, if there is no initial velocity v_z, there will be nothing to make z other than zero), the force is directed along the line joining the planet to the sun, as shown in Fig. 9–5.

From this figure we see that the horizontal component of the force is related to the complete force in the same manner as the horizontal distance x is to the complete hypotenuse r, because the two triangles are similar. Also, if x is positive,

F_x is negative. That is, $F_x/|F| = -x/r$, or $F_x = -|F|x/r = -GMmx/r^3$. Now we use the dynamical law to find that this force component is equal to the mass of the planet times the rate of change of its velocity in the x-direction. Thus we find the following laws:

$$m(dv_x/dt) = -GMmx/r^3,$$
$$m(dv_y/dt) = -GMmy/r^3,$$
$$r = \sqrt{x^2 + y^2}. \tag{9.17}$$

This, then, is the set of equations we must solve. Again, in order to simplify the numerical work, we shall suppose that the unit of time, or the mass of the sun, has been so adjusted (or luck is with us) that $GM \equiv 1$. For our specific example we shall suppose that the initial position of the planet is at $x = 0.500$ and $y = 0.000$, and that the velocity is all in the y-direction at the start, and is of magnitude 1.6300. Now how do we make the calculation? We again make a table with columns for the time, the x-position, the x-velocity v_x, and the x-acceleration a_x; then, separated by a double line, three columns for position, velocity, and acceleration in the y-direction. In order to get the accelerations we are going to need Eq. (9.17); it tells us that the acceleration in the x-direction is $-x/r^3$, and the acceleration in the y-direction is $-y/r^3$, and that r is the square root of $x^2 + y^2$. Thus, given x and y, we must do a little calculating on the side, taking the square root of the sum of the squares to find r and then, to get ready to calculate the two accelerations, it is useful also to evaluate $1/r^3$. This work can be done rather easily by using a table of squares, cubes, and reciprocals: then we need only multiply x by $1/r^3$, which we do on a slide rule.

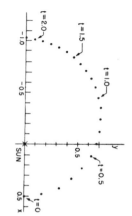

Fig. 9–6. The calculated motion of a planet around the sun.

Our calculation thus proceeds by the following steps, using time intervals $\epsilon = 0.100$: Initial values at $t = 0$:

$$x(0) = 0.500 \qquad y(0) = 0.000$$
$$v_x(0) = 0.000 \qquad v_y(0) = +1.630$$

From these we find:

$$r(0) = 0.500 \qquad 1/r^3(0) = 8.000$$
$$a_x = -4.000 \qquad a_y = 0.000$$

Thus we may calculate the velocities $v_x(0.05)$ and $v_y(0.05)$:

$$v_x(0.05) = 0.000 - 4.000 \times 0.050 = -0.200;$$
$$v_y(0.05) = 1.630 + 0.000 \times 0.100 = 1.630.$$

Now our main calculations begin:

$$x(0.1) = 0.500 - 0.20 \times 0.1 \quad = \quad 0.480$$
$$y(0.1) = 0.0 + 1.63 \times 0.1 \quad = \quad 0.163$$
$$r = \sqrt{0.480^2 + 0.163^2} \quad = \quad 0.507$$
$$1/r^3 \quad = \quad 7.67$$
$$a_x(0.1) = 0.480 \times 7.67 \quad = \quad -3.68$$
$$a_y(0.1) = -0.163 \times 7.70 \quad = \quad -1.256$$
$$v_x(0.15) = -0.200 - 3.68 \times 0.1 \quad = \quad -0.568$$
$$v_y(0.15) = 1.630 - 1.26 \times 0.1 \quad = \quad 1.505$$
$$x(0.2) = 0.480 - 0.568 \times 0.1 \quad = \quad 0.423$$
$$y(0.2) = 0.163 + 1.50 \times 0.1 \quad = \quad 0.313$$

etc.

In this way we obtain the values given in Table 9–2, and in 20 steps or so we have chased the planet halfway around the sun! In Fig. 9–6 are plotted the x- and y-coordinates given in Table 9–2. The dots represent the positions at the succession of times a tenth of a unit apart; we see that at the start the planet moves rapidly and at the end it moves slowly, and so the shape of the curve is determined. Thus we see that we *really do* know how to calculate the motion of planets!

Now let us see how we can calculate the motion of Neptune, Jupiter, Uranus, or any other planet. If we have a great many planets, and let the sun move too, can we do the same thing? Of course we can. We calculate the force on a particular planet, let us say planet number i, which has a position x_i, y_i, z_i ($i = 1$ may represent the sun, $i = 2$ Mercury, $i = 3$ Venus, and so on). We must know the positions of all the planets. The force acting on one is due to all the other bodies which are located, let us say, at positions x_j, y_j, z_j. Therefore the equations are

$$m_i \frac{dv_{ix}}{dt} = \sum_{j=1}^{N} - \frac{Gm_i m_j (x_i - x_j)}{r_{ij}^3},$$

$$m_i \frac{dv_{iy}}{dt} = \sum_{j=1}^{N} - \frac{Gm_i m_j (y_i - y_j)}{r_{ij}^3},$$

$$m_i \frac{dv_{iz}}{dt} = \sum_{j=1}^{N} - \frac{Gm_i m_j (z_i - z_j)}{r_{ij}^3}. \tag{9.18}$$

Table 9-2

Solution of $dv_x/dt = -x/r^3$, $dv_y/dt = -y/r^3$, $r = \sqrt{x^2 + y^2}$.

Interval: $\epsilon = 0.100$

Orbit $v_y = 1.63$ $v_z = 0$ $x = 0.5$ $y = 0$ at $t = 0$

t	x	v_x	a_x	y	v_y	a_y	r	$1/r^3$
0.0	0.500	−0.200	−4.00	0.000	1.630	0.00	0.500	8.000
0.1	0.480	−0.568	−3.68	0.163	1.505	−1.25	0.507	7.675
0.2	0.423	−0.859	−2.91	0.313	1.290	−2.15	0.526	6.873
0.3	0.337	−1.055	−1.96	0.442	1.033	−2.57	0.556	5.824
0.4	0.232	−1.166	−1.11	0.545	0.771	−2.62	0.592	4.81
0.5	0.115	−1.211	−0.453	0.622	0.526	−2.45	0.633	3.942
0.6	−0.006	−1.209	+0.020	0.675	0.306	−2.20	0.675	3.252
0.7	−0.127	−1.175	+0.344	0.706	0.115	−1.91	0.717	2.712
0.8	−0.245	−1.119	+0.562	0.718	−0.049	−1.64	0.758	2.296
0.9	−0.357	−1.048	+0.705	0.713	−0.190	−1.41	0.797	1.975
1.0	−0.462	−0.968	+0.796	0.694	−0.310	−1.20	0.834	1.723
1.1	−0.559	−0.882	+0.858	0.663	−0.412	−1.02	0.867	1.535
1.2	−0.647	−0.792	+0.90	0.622	−0.499	−0.86	0.897	1.385
1.3	−0.726	−0.700	+0.92	0.572	−0.570	−0.72	0.924	1.267
1.4	−0.796	−0.607	+0.93	0.515	−0.630	−0.60	0.948	1.173
1.5	−0.857	−0.513	+0.94	0.452	−0.680	−0.50	0.969	1.099
1.6	−0.908	−0.418	+0.95	0.384	−0.720	−0.40	0.986	1.043
1.7	−0.950	−0.323	+0.95	0.312	−0.751	−0.31	1.000	1.000
1.8	−0.982	−0.228	+0.95	0.237	−0.773	−0.23	1.010	0.970
1.9	−1.005	−0.113	+0.95	0.160	−0.778	−0.15	1.018	0.948
2.0	−1.018	−0.037	+0.96	0.081	−0.796	−0.08	1.021	0.939
2.1	−1.022	+0.058	+0.96	0.001	−0.796	0.00	1.022	0.936
2.2	−1.016		+0.96	−0.079	−0.789	+0.07	1.019	0.945
2.3								

Crossed x-axis at 2.101 sec, ∴ period = 4.20 sec.

$v_x = 0$ at 2.086 sec.

Cross x at 1.022, ∴ semimajor axis = $\dfrac{1.022 + 0.500}{2} = 0.761$.

$v_y = 0.796$.

Predicted time $\pi(0.761)^{3/2} = \pi(0.663) = 2.082$.

Further, we define r_{ij} as the distance between the two planets i and j; this is equal to

$$r_{ij} = \sqrt{(x_i - x_j)^2 + (y_i - y_j)^2 + (z_i - z_j)^2}. \qquad (9.19)$$

Also, $\sum$ means a sum over all values of j—all other bodies—except, of course, for $j = i$. Thus all we have to do is to make more columns, *lots* more columns. We need nine columns for the motions of Jupiter, nine for the motions of Saturn, and so on. Then when we have all initial positions and velocities we can calculate all the accelerations from Eq. (9.18) by first calculating all the distances, using Eq. (9.19). How long will it take to do it? If you do it at home, it will take a very long time! But in modern times we have machines which do arithmetic very rapidly; a very good computing machine may take 1 microsecond, that is, a millionth of a second, to do an addition. To do a multiplication takes longer, say 10 microseconds. It may be that in one cycle of calculation, depending on the problem, we may have 30 multiplications, or something like that, so one cycle will take 300 microseconds. That means that we can do 3000 cycles of computation per second. In order to get an accuracy, of, say, one part in a billion, we would need 4×10^5 cycles to correspond to one revolution of a planet around the sun. That corresponds to a computation time of 130 seconds or about two minutes. Thus it take only two minutes to follow Jupiter around the sun, with all the perturbations of all the planets correct to one part in a billion, by this method! (It turns out that the error varies about as the square of the interval ϵ. If we make the interval a thousand times smaller, it is a million times more accurate. So, let us make the interval 10,000 times smaller.)

So, as we said, we began this chapter not knowing how to calculate even the motion of a mass on a spring. Now, armed with the tremendous power of Newton's laws, we can not only calculate such simple motions but also, given only a machine to handle the arithmetic, even the tremendously complex motions of the planets, to as high a degree of precision as we wish!

CHAPTER 3

COMMENTS ON VELOCITY

Because we shall frequently refer to the chapter on motion from the *Feynman Lectures on Physics*, for brevity we shall use only the name Feynman to represent the coauthorship of Feynman, Leighton, and Sands.

The Feynman chapter is largely independent of the chapters which precede it in the original text. Some details in the chapter need not concern us. For example, you do not need to know enough calculus to show that Feynman's Eq. 9–10 is a solution for Eq. 9–9. However, it is important to follow Feynman in arriving at the basic equations for calculation, both for the harmonic oscillator and for gravitational attraction. If you can do this, you should proceed to the computer programs for Feynman's calculations in Chapter 4. The present discussion may be useful for those who need additional assistance in understanding acceleration, velocity, and the derivative.

Figure 3-1

Consider a particle moving in a plane. We assume that we have a repeatable motion. When we first watch the complete motion, we note that it traces a curve in the plane; we could mark the curve and obtain a drawing like that shown in Fig. 3–1.

So far this is only a description of the motion, because we are not measuring. Two types of measurements are needed for an accurate description of motion. First are measurements with a clock; because the particle is moving along the curve, it is at different positions at different times. Using a clock, we can associate a unique time number with a position of the particle. You can imagine experimental arrangements that do this for many positions. One possibility is to attach a small rapidly, and consistently, blinking neon light to the moving object. A photographic time exposure of the motion would give a series of points known to be at equal time intervals from one another. Calling the time at any one position the "zero" of time, we can assign times to the other events. (The assumption that for every position there is a time goes beyond experimental resources, and requires additional theoretical assumptions; but we ignore this, assuming that we can associate a time with each position.)

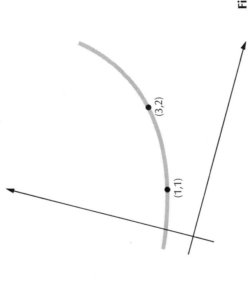

Figure 3-2

So far we have used the term "position" to mean an identifiable point on the page, but you probably know that position, as well as time, can be associated with numbers by a measuring process. The most common procedure is to establish a Cartesian coordinate system in the plane of motion, i.e., a pair of lines at right angles to each other, each with a designated positive direction. These lines are often called x and y, or, alternatively, x_1 and x_2. The choice of a Cartesian coordinate system is arbitrary, since one can draw many such pairs of directed lines in the plane, and different coordinate systems associate different pairs of numbers with the same point. Some of the most interesting results in modern physics arise because different coordinate systems are possible, but we will not be concerned with this. Figure 3-2 displays the motion under discussion again, but this time the coordinate system is also shown.

Given a coordinate system, we can establish a one-to-one correspondence between points in the plane and pairs of numbers. The usual procedure is to draw lines from the point in question perpendicular to the x_1- and x_2-axes. Then the distances from the point to the coordinate axes furnish a pair of numbers; each number is positive if the point lies toward the positive direction on the axis and negative if the point lies toward the opposite direction. In the coordinate system shown in Fig. 3–2 two positions along the curve have been given the coordinate pairs (1,1) and (3,2).

The calculation of average velocity requires knowledge of the particle's position at two times. These positions can be the same, in which case the average velocity is zero, but usually they are different. Suppose that the first position has the coordinates (1,1), and the particle is there at time $t = 4$; further, let the coordinates of the second position be (3,2) and the time there be $t = 7$. We want to determine the quantity we can reasonably call the average velocity between the two times. The usual (vague) statement is that the velocity is the rate of change of position with respect to time. Since there are two position coordinates and since each might change, we have two "velocities" to consider. The first of these is associated with the x_1-component, the second with the x_2-component. The expression "rate of change with respect to time" has different meanings for different people; we need to "translate" it into a more precise mathematical statement. In the present case the *change* in the x_1-component of position is $(3 - 1)$, or 2. It is not obvious what "rate" and "with respect to time" means. Three units of time elapsed between the two positions. If you make the correct association of rate with division, you would probably divide the change in the x_1-position, 2 in this example, by the change in the time, 3. This would agree with the standard usage of the term "average velocity" for the x_1-component, and we would have

$$2 \div 3 = 0.666.$$

Generalizing from this one example, we can say that the average velocity of a component of velocity is the ratio of the change in the corresponding position component to the change in time.

Problem 1. In the example just discussed, what is the average velocity in the x_2-direction between time $t = 4$ and time $t = 7$?

In a one-dimensional problem, such as the harmonic oscillator, the particle is known to move along a line, and therefore we do not need two axes; rather we use the line itself, with an arbitrarily chosen origin and positive direction, as the coordinate system. Thus there is one position number and only one average velocity, rather than a pair as in two dimensions.

INSTANTANEOUS VELOCITY

A careful discussion of (instantaneous) velocity will not be attempted, since it would require mathematical apparatus concerning the concept of limit; but an intuitive conception of velocity, using the concept of average velocity, is not difficult. Imagine that we observe the motion over and over again, each time noting details on only two positions. One of these is always the position at time $t = 4$, while the other position might be $t = 6$, then $t = 5$, etc. We keep computing average velocity for each pair, always using the $t = 4$ point as the first position. We cannot have both points at $t = 4$, because this would result in the mathematically meaningless expression 0/0. But as long as the second point is a slight time later, the measurement is always possible in principle, ignoring any possible atomic effects. For each pair we can compute the average velocity just as we did above. What happens in almost all cases of actual physical motion is that the second point is taken closer and closer to the first point and successive calculations of average velocity differ less and less. Mathematicians can with ease concoct situations in which this does not happen, but such convergence is an empirical observation for actual motions. It is the average velocity computed for smaller and smaller separations of time that we call *the velocity*, or the *instantaneous velocity*. In the two-dimensional case two components of velocity, as well as two components of average velocity, are defined, and for one-dimensional motion the velocity has one component.

We can express this result more symbolically. Suppose that the two coordinates of some position are represented by x_1 and x_2, and that the time when the particle is at this position is t. To designate the position and time for some second particle event, we can put a prime on each of the quantities, i.e., the coordinates will be (x_1', x_2') and time t'. Then one component of the average velocity between the two events is given by

$$\frac{x_1' - x_1}{t' - t}.$$

A similar expression can be given for the other component. The derivative notation, such as that used in Feynman, is intended to express the "limit" case, where the two times, t and t', in this expression are allowed to become closer and closer together. For our purposes we write

$$\frac{dx_1}{dt} = \lim_{t \to t'} \left(\frac{x_1' - x_1}{t' - t} \right),$$

although this is not a precise expression, since we have not given a careful definition of limit.

Feynman replaces instantaneous velocity by average velocity over a very small time interval ϵ, relying on the empirical result that if the time interval is taken small enough, then the average velocity closely approximates the instantaneous velocity.

The Harmonic Oscillator — Numerical Solution

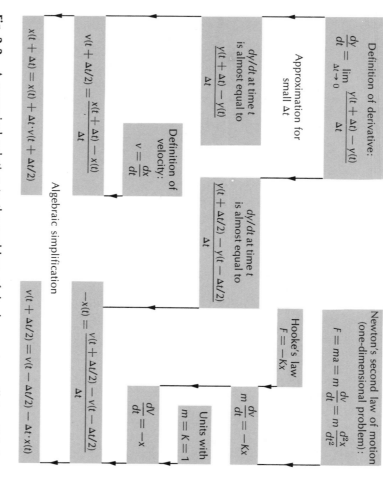

Definition of derivative:
$$\frac{dy}{dt} = \lim_{\Delta t \to 0} \frac{y(t+\Delta t) - y(t)}{\Delta t}$$

Approximation for small Δt

dy/dt at time t is almost equal to
$$\frac{y(t+\Delta t) - y(t)}{\Delta t}$$

dy/dt at time t is almost equal to
$$\frac{y(t+\Delta t/2) - y(t-\Delta t/2)}{\Delta t}$$

Definition of velocity:
$$v = \frac{dx}{dt}$$

$$v(t+\Delta t/2) = \frac{x(t+\Delta t) - x(t)}{\Delta t}$$

Algebraic simplification

$$x(t+\Delta t) = x(t) + \Delta t \cdot v(t+\Delta t/2)$$

Newton's second law of motion (one-dimensional problem):
$$F = ma = m\frac{dv}{dt} = m\frac{d^2x}{dt^2}$$

Hooke's law
$$F = -Kx$$

$$m\frac{dv}{dt} = -Kx$$

Units with $m = K = 1$

$$\frac{dV}{dt} = -x$$

$$-x(t) = \frac{v(t+\Delta t/2) - v(t-\Delta t/2)}{\Delta t}$$

$$v(t+\Delta t/2) = v(t-\Delta t/2) - \Delta t \cdot x(t)$$

Fig. 3-3. A numerical solution to the problem of the harmonic oscillator. This is one way to arrive at Feynman's approximation equations.

So in place of the expression

$$dx_i/dt = v_i,$$

Feynman would write the approximation

$$\frac{x_i' - x_i}{t' - t} = v_i$$

or, equivalently,

$$x_i' = x_i + v_i(t' - t).$$

Similar remarks hold with respect to the acceleration and velocity, which stand in the same relation to each other as velocity and position.

Feynman also uses "second derivative notation" to indicate, as usual, the derivative of a derivative:

$$\frac{d^2 x_1}{dt^2} = \frac{d}{dt}\left(\frac{dx_1}{dt}\right).$$

The flow chart in Fig. 3–3 illustrates one way to arrive at Feynman's approximation equations.

CHAPTER 4

FORTRAN AND MECHANICS

Although Feynman's tactics in finding the motion of a mass on a spring, or of a planet are readily understood, much calculation is needed to obtain the tables of results, Tables 9–1 and 9–2.

Problem 2. Verify Feynman's results for the harmonic oscillator for the times $t = 1.0$ and $t = 1.1$.

Problem 3. Verify the results in Table 9–2, gravitational motion, for the time $t = 1.1$.

Problem 4. Assume that you have hired a calculational assistant who has the abilities listed in Chapter 1, but has no familiarity with classical mechanics. Write a detailed set of instructions for the assistant to follow in obtaining the approximate motion of a harmonic oscillator using the approach given by Feynman. Assume that you want a listing of the results up to time $t = 10$. Allow for the possibility that you may want the assistant to use several different values of the "step," Δt (ϵ in Feynman). Remember that you must describe not only the details of the calculation but also the form in which you want the answer.

THE HARMONIC OSCILLATOR

With the preceding chapters serving as background, we shall now see how we can use a computer and the FORTRAN language to perform lengthy calculations. We begin by presenting a FORTRAN program which follows Feynman's procedure for obtaining the approximate motion of a harmonic oscillator, with a few changes to be discussed later, and then we discuss this program in terms of the desired calculation. The program is shown in Fig. 4–1.

You will probably recognize some steps in this FORTRAN program from your study of Feynman's treatment of the harmonic oscillator problem, but as with any language that you do not know, much will seem unfamiliar. The program is a collection of sentences or statements which are, presumably, grammatically correct according to the syntactical rules of FORTRAN. Each line is a single statement,

```
   1    TYPE 2
   2    FORMAT (30HNATURAL SCIENCE 110 — F/M = -X /14HTYPE IN DELTAT)
        ACCEPT 3, DELT
   3    FORMAT ( F5.3 )
   C    FIVE PLACES ARE RESERVED FOR DELT, WITH THREE DECIMAL POINTS
        TYPE 100
  100   FORMAT ( /15HFEYNMAN METHOD  /   )
   4    TYPE 4
        FORMAT (5H TIME, 12X 9HAPPROX X      ,
        114X 9H APPROX V , 3X 7H COS(T))
   C    WE SET INITIAL CONDITIONS FOR TIME, POSITION, AND VELOCITY
   C    T = 0.
        X = 1.
        V = 0.
        TP = .1
   C    CALCULATION OF THE INITIAL HALF STEP IN THE VELOCITY
        V = V - X * DELT / 2.
   C    MAIN CALCULATION BEGINS IN SENTENCE FIVE
   5    X = X + DELT * V
        T = T + DELT
        V = V - DELT * X
   C
   6    IF (T - TP) 5, 6, 6
        TP = TP + .1
        XE = COSF(T)
   7    TYPE 7, T, X, XE, V
        FORMAT (F6.3, 12X F8.5, 25X F8.5 /41X F8.5)
        IF (SENSE SWITCH 2) 8, 5
   C    SENSE SWITCH TWO OFF FOR CONTINUING CALCULATION
   C    SENSE SWITCH ONE ON STOPS PROGRAM
   8    IF (SENSE SWITCH 1) 9, 10
   9    STOP
  10    PAUSE
        GO TO 1
        END
```

Figure 4-1

with one exception, which will be discussed later. Except for branches, which are to be discussed later, the statements are executed in the order written. Some of the statements, but not all, are identified by numbers; usually FORTRAN statements that are numbered are ones that are referred to by other statements in the program. For bookkeeping purposes, you could number any sentence in a FORTRAN program; these numbers serve as names or *labels* for the statements. The numbers need not be in order; it is not necessary to start with one and label succeeding statements sequentially, since the numbers do not determine the sequence of the program.

This program is made up of only a few basic kinds of sentences. A "C," for comment, which precedes some of the sentences, is not intended for the computer but for human readers of the program. The computer ignores any sentence beginning with C; however, it will type or print it if a listing of the whole program is requested. In one line a C is used with no statement following it; this simply serves to provide a line of space in the program. In other places in the program the comment sentence gives information about what is happening at that particular stage in the program. Comment statements can be used freely in a FORTRAN program. We use the comment statements for pedagogical purposes, but they are more important in programming than one might initially suspect. If others are to use your program, they need to know what you are trying to do in the different stages of the program. Even if you are the only user, you may appreciate such information when you use the program again after a long interval.

Three statements of the form TYPE X, where X is a statement number, occur early in the program. When the program is run, the first statement, TYPE 2, will generate a heading. Statement 2 is a FORMAT statement; the net effect of statement 1 is to type or print the heading contained in 2. In the first part of the FORMAT statement, 30H means that the 30 characters (including spaces) following the H are to be printed. A slash (/) in a FORMAT statement tells the computer to return the carriage on the typewriter or to go ahead to the next line of the printer, and 14H indicates that 14 characters are to be printed; the next 14 numbers, letters, special symbols, and spaces following the H in the statement. The purpose of this heading is to identify the page. Such bookkeeping practices may not seem important, but when you are getting large amounts of information from the computer, possibly to be referred to years later, full documentation is important; each page should be identified and its program named. With larger machines the computer may automatically supply this documentation.

The third statement in the program, which has no statement number, is an ACCEPT command. It also refers to a FORMAT statement, statement 3. The ACCEPT command instructs the computer to wait for information that will be entered on the typewriter. In this case it will be a number which will be called DELT in the program. DELT represents the time step Δt (ϵ in Feynman) in the program, since the Greek letters delta and epsilon are not present on most computer typewriters and printers; usually only capital Roman letters are available. DELT is *not the* product of four variable names as you might expect from your experience with algebra, but instead identifies a *single* variable name; multiplication is shown by an explicit multiplication sign, an asterisk, within a FORTRAN program. Variables can be identified with names comprised of several characters; the first is always a letter, but the others can be either letters or numbers. The precise number of letters and numbers allowed differs from implementation to implementation. The ACCEPT statement also mentions a FORMAT statement, as do most FORTRAN statements concerning input or output. Later we shall explain the structure of FORMAT statements, which control during output the location of the material on the line, the number of significant figures, and the number of places needed to the left of the decimal point. During input they specify how the material is to be punched on the card.

From the program you can see that about half of the statements contain equal signs. Such statements look like equations and, in fact, are a kind of equation. It was the desirability of using formula-type expressions directly in computer programs that initially led to the development of FORTRAN and other algebraic languages. Each of the statements containing an equal sign has a single variable on the left-hand side of the equation. These statements direct the computer to compute the expression on the right-hand side of the equation, using values of the variable stored in memory, and to assign the value obtained to the variable on the left-hand side, storing it in the appropriate location in memory. Thus T = 0. assigns the value 0 to the variable T, and the next statement assigns the value 1 to the variable X.

The use of decimal points with zeros and ones may seem peculiar to the reader unfamiliar with FORTRAN. These decimal points indicate one of the two forms of numbers and variables allowed in the FORTRAN language. In a *floating-point number* a decimal point is associated with the number; in the other form, the *fixed point*, the quantity is an integer and is written without a decimal point. These two forms of numbers are each treated differently by the computer. For the present we shall use only floating-point numbers, with a decimal point. The FORTRAN manner of distinguishing between floating-point variables and fixed-point variables concerns the first letter: A variable which begins with I, J, K, L, M, or N is a fixed-point variable; others are floating point. None of the variables in our program begin with these letters, since all of them have been written as floating-point variables.

The arithmetic statements we have considered so far are very simple in that they assign a number to a particular variable. However, there are complicated statements containing equal signs within the program, statements which involve computation. Let us look at statement 5. As an algebraic sentence it would be rather strange; your temptation may be, treating it as an equation, to subtract X from both sides, which would result in the expression DELT*V = 0. But this is *not* the intent of the FORTRAN statement. The variables in FORTRAN expressions are in effect names for particular locations in the memory of the computer. Thus X will correspond to some location in memory, and DELT and V to other locations. Sentence 5 not only specifies the computation to be carried out but also informs the computer where the numbers are located in memory and where in memory the result is to be stored after the computation is finished. In working the program the computer will find three numbers in memory, X, DELT, and V; it will then carry out the computation indicated on the right-hand side of the equation. The plus sign, of course, is simply the usual mathematical plus sign and the asterisk is the FORTRAN multiplication sign. After the computation is completed, the instruction asks that the resulting number be stored in the location designated by the variable X. Thus the net effect of this operation in the program is to change the value of X stored in the memory. The original value of X is used for the computation on the right-hand side of the statement, and this produces a new value of X which then "erases" and replaces the original value of X. As indicated by the comment, statement 5 and the two sentences following it represent the main part of the calculation. You can see, comparing these three statements with the procedure in Feynman, that the statements are instructing the computer to calculate the new X, the new V, and the new T—the new position, the new velocity, and the new time. The new values are then stored in memory, replacing the old values of the variables.

The IF statements in the program have no obvious meaning if you are unfamiliar with FORTRAN, but you might suspect that what they tell the computer to do depends upon certain conditions. This branching aspect is indeed their purpose within the program. Two kinds of IF statements are used in the harmonic oscillator problem. The first one, immediately preceding statement 6, has an arithmetic expression in parentheses. Following this arithmetic expression are three statement numbers, separated by commas. When an IF statement is encountered in a program the value of the expression inside the parentheses is computed; i.e., the necessary variables are obtained from memory and the arithmetic calculation indicated is carried out. If the resulting expression is negative, then the program goes to the first statement of the three, in this case statement 5; if it is zero it goes to the second statement, 6; and, finally, if it is positive, it goes to the third statement, here also statement 6. These three statement numbers may be different, or any two may be the same. There is no necessity for all three to be the same.

The calculational purpose of the IF statement may not be clear to you, since it involves a decision not arising in Feynman's calculation. He works only with a time step of 0.1, but we want to be able to try other steps, including very small ones, entering them by the typewriter. If we were to type or print the result of the calculations for each step, that could entail a vast amount of output. What we want is a sampling. The variable TP in the program is used to control output. TP is initially 0.1; and because of the IF statement there is no output until T equals 0.1. Then TP is increased by one-tenth and, similarly, typeout does not occur until T equals or exceeds this new value of 0.2.

The statement following sentence 7 and statement 8 in the program are another and somewhat simpler kind of IF statement, the IF SENSE SWITCH statement. The parentheses in these statements contain not an arithmetic expression as in the previous IF, but rather a reference to a numbered switch. These numbers correspond to physical two-position switches called *sense switches* on the console of the computer. The two numbers following the parentheses are again statement numbers. The program is to go to the first of these if the sense switch is on and to the second if it is off. This condition allows the person at the console of the program to affect the course of the program by throwing the switch on the console. You should be able to follow the comment statements associated with these two sentences in order to see what they do. Not all computers have sense switches, so this type of statement is not always available in FORTRAN. It is seldom possible to use a large computer in this fashion, since the programmer is usually not the computer operator.

We have mentioned output of results but have not looked at the sentence which produces this output. It is the second statement after statement 6. It not only mentions a FORMAT statement number, as did the previous input-output sentences we have seen, but it also lists the variables whose values we want typed or printed. As we have previously indicated, the associated FORMAT statement describes the positioning of these variables on the page—location, number of decimal points, etc.

The one way this program differs from the calculation presented in Feynman occurs in the statement which follows statement 6, XE = COSF(T). Note also that the program requests that the value of XE be printed whenever we print X. The expression on the right-hand side is self-revealing; it means the cosine function of the variable T, a function already familiar to some of you. We are not indicating why we are computing the cosine of the time, although the reason may have occurred to you from the study of Feynman, particularly if you plotted additional values; the cosine is an exact solution to the problem.

Problem 5. If you already know enough calculus to differentiate simple functions, show that $x = \cos(t)$ is a solution of the differential equation

$$d^2x/dt^2 = -x,$$

the harmonic oscillator equation. Show also that this function satisfies Feynman's initial conditions ($t = 0$) for the harmonic oscillator problem.

The computation of the cosine has a pedagogical purpose; if this program is run on a computer, then the exact solution will also be obtained and it can be compared with the approximate solution.

We should make it clear that the computer does not have as part of its basic circuitry the ability to calculate the cosine function, nor does it store the values of the cosine for all possible arguments. Instead it stores a program supplied by the manufacturer for calculating the cosine of any number to whatever degree of accuracy is required. Whenever a program calls for a cosine, the stored program goes into action and the cosine is computed for that particular value. The cosine need not be used in a statement by itself, but may be part of an elaborate arithmetic calculation. FORTRAN includes a number of such *library functions*—common functions that are used often in scientific computation. The list of available functions differs from one computer center to another.

Some statements in the program are almost self-explanatory, because of the use of English words in FORTRAN. GO TO 1, just before the end of the program, sends the computer to the beginning of the program, statement 1. Thus it creates a *branch* in the program, a branch which is unconditional in that it always occurs whenever the program reaches this point. The difference between PAUSE and STOP is not obvious to the uninitiated. STOP represents an exit point from the program. If a computer reaches a command saying STOP, it "understands" that this program is finished and that it can, if it is so working, go ahead to other programs. On the other hand, PAUSE keeps the computer within the same program. It puts the machine in a resting or waiting state, waiting for the operator to push the start button. When the button is pushed, the program goes on to the statement after the PAUSE, in this case the GO TO command. One is not likely to use PAUSE with a large computer, because computer time is usually too valuable to allow the machine to be idle.

A special situation holds in statement 4 and the line following in the harmonic oscillator program. The second line is a continuation of statement 4. Later, when we discuss punched cards, a common way to enter FORTRAN programs into the computer, we shall find that since a card holds only a limited collection of symbols, a long statement may not fit on the card. Hence FORTRAN has a special provision for lengthy statements—we can indicate that a card contains a statement which is continued from another card. The "1" which is out of line at the left of the second line of statement 4 serves as a continuation sign. Any symbol other than a zero or a blank can be used to denote a continuation, and there can usually be more than one continuation card, the exact number depending on the computer used.

We have covered most of the statements in the program. Some of them may not be entirely clear to you, particularly the FORMAT statements, which were not described in detail, but with some study, usage, and comparison with Feynman's harmonic oscillator calculation, you should begin to recognize the value of FOR-TRAN as a language.

Problem 6. Show that the program we have been discussing is essentially equivalent to Feynman's calculation for the harmonic oscillator problem. Outline the steps the computer will perform. Can you think of any convenient way to represent these steps diagrammatically?

Problem 7. Why do we not need to write "$x(t)$" and "$x(t + \epsilon)$," as Feynman does, but only "X'?

Problem 8. When Feynman first approaches the numerical solution of the harmonic oscillator problem, he suggests a slightly different method than that he later uses. His first method is one which involves the calculation of positions and velocities at the *same* time. Feynman claims that his modification improves the accuracy with little additional work. How would you modify the FORTRAN program given here for the harmonic oscillator so that it would carry out the calculation by Feynman's *first* method?

Problem 9. Modify the program for a computer with no console sense switches. Assume that each calculation will end at $t = 5$.

Problem 10. Modify the FORTRAN program so that it works for a *damped* harmonic oscillator, one in which there is a force term proportional to and opposed to the velocity in addition to the distance-dependent force. The two forces are added to give the total force. If you have access to a computer, determine the dependence of the motion on the value of the damping constant, the proportionality factor in the velocity-dependent force term.

PLANETARY MOTION

For a second example of a FORTRAN program we shall consider motion under an inverse square central force. This is the gravitational case, perhaps a planetary or satellite problem, where one massive body can be considered to have a fixed position (the force center), and the force on the second body varies inversely as the square of the distance between the two bodies. As in Feynman the differential equations which determine the motion of the second body are

$$\frac{d^2 x_1}{dt^2} = -\frac{x_1}{r^3} \quad \text{and} \quad \frac{d^2 x_2}{dt^2} = -\frac{x_2}{r^3},$$

where $r = \sqrt{(x_1)^2 + (x_2)^2}$, and the mass and gravitational constant are taken to be unity. Note the use of x_1 and x_2 as coordinate names rather than x and y, a minor *fortran and mechanics*

```
    1    TYPE 2
    2    FORMAT (34H NATURAL SCIENCE 110 — GRAVITATION/8H DELT = )
         ACCEPT 3, DELT
    3    FORMAT (F5.3)
         TYPE 500
  500    FORMAT (48HTYPE INITIAL CONDITIONS FOR X1, X2, VI, AND V2     )
         TYPE 501
  501    FORMAT (20HFIVE SPACES FOR EACH        )
         ACCEPT 4, X1, X2, V1, V2
    4    FORMAT (4F5.3 )
         TYPE 10
   10    FORMAT (30H INITIAL CONDITIONS ( T = 0)     )
         TYPE 5, X1, X2, V1, V2
    5    FORMAT (4HX1 =     , F6.3, 2X 4HX2 =     , F6.3, 2X 4HV1 =     , F6.3, 2X
    1    4HV2 =     , F6.3   )
         TYPE 11
   11    FORMAT (45H UNITS — MASS AND GRAVITATIONAL CONSTANT ONE     )
         E = (V1 * V1 + V2 * V2) / 2. — 1. / ((X1 * X1 + X2 * X2) ** .5)
         TYPE 12 , E
   12    FORMAT (17H TOTAL ENERGY =        ,F8.3   )
         TYPE 6
    6    FORMAT (/4HTIME, 14X 2HX1, 10X 2HX2, 10X 2HV1, 10X 2HV2   )
         T = 0.
         TP = .1
    F    = DELT / (((X1 * X1 + X2 * X2) ** (1.5)) * 2.)
         V1 = V1 — X1 * F
         V2 = V2 — X2 * F
         X1 = X1 + V1 * DELT
         X2 = X2 + V2 * DELT
    7    F = DELT / ((X1 * X1 + X2 * X2) ** (1.5))
         V1 = V1 — X1 * F
         V2 = V2 — X2 * F
         T = T + DELT
         IF (T — TP) 7, 8, 8
    8    TP = TP + .1
         IF (SENSE SWITCH 2) 7, 90
         SENSE SWITCH TWO OFF FOR TYPEOUT
   90    TYPE 9, T, X1, X2, V1, V2
    9    FORMAT (F5.1, 8X F9.5, 3X F9.5 / 35X F9.5, 3X F9.5 )
         IF (SENSE SWITCH 1) 27, 7
   27    IF (SENSE SWITCH 3) 13, 14
         SENSE SWITCH ONE OFF FOR CONTINUATION OF CALCULATION
         SENSE SWITCH THREE ON STOPS PROGRAM, OFF BEGINS AGAIN FOR NEW
         INITIAL CONDITIONS
   13    CALL EXIT
   14    PAUSE
         GO TO 1
         END
```

Figure 4–2

difference. Also, since we are assuming that the motion takes place in a plane, there are two Newtonian equations rather than one as in the harmonic oscillator problem.

The approach in the FORTRAN program is similar to Feynman's but there are some differences. Because the calculation is not a hand calculation, it is not necessary to calculate or to print all the columns in Table 9–2; the arrangement there is presumably intended to assist a human calculator rather than a machine. The FOR-TRAN program for the gravitational force problem is shown in Fig. 4–2.

The two asterisks placed side by side have a special meaning in FORTRAN: they represent exponentiation, so in the calculation for F the expression in parentheses is raised to the 1.5 (= 3/2) power. FORTRAN is strictly a linear language in that all symbols lie on the same line. As in any program we try to avoid doing the same calculation too many times. Since $(\Delta t/r^3)$ occurs in the equations for both v_1 and v_2, we compute it before encountering these equations, and then use the result in both equations. To do this we assign a name, F, as a variable internal to the program.

Again, as with both of Feynman's calculations, there are "starting" equations which calculate the first half-step in the velocity; in the program these are the three lines just above sentence 7. This program differs from our previous programs in that it allows us to enter by the console values of x_1, x_2, v_1, and v_2 at time zero, the initial values of position and velocity, so that we can calculate for various choices of initial conditions. An alternative procedure, which involves changing the command ACCEPT to READ, would be to have the computer "read" a data card containing each set of initial values. Using the typewriter or data cards allows us to numerically experiment with different initial values and thus determine how the motion depends on initial conditions.

Problem 11. By means of a suitable diagram, show the logical structure of the preceding program.

Problem 12. The program calculates and types out a quantity called "E." Feynman does not calculate the value of the quantity. Write this expression in standard algebraic notation. You may be able to determine the physical connotation of E from previous experience; if not, you can find a "name" for E within the program. If you can run the program on a computer, find how its value affects the result of the calculation.

Problem 13. Suppose that a particle moves in a plane under the action of a force which varies directly as the distance from a given point, and that the force is always directed toward a fixed point. Modify the FORTRAN program for gravitational force so that it applies to this new situation. Are you familiar with any physical systems which have forces of this kind?

fortran and mechanics

Problem 14. One check on the accuracy of the approximation in any central force problem is to determine whether equal areas are being swept out in equal times by a line connecting the particle and the force center. This is a property of any central force motion, as was shown by Newton in the first Proposition in the *Principia*. Modify the gravitational program so that it calculates and prints information of this kind.

CHAPTER 5

LANGUAGES AND COMPUTERS

As an introduction to the FORTRAN language we have presented FORTRAN programs for two problems solved in Feynman by numerical techniques; however, the relation of programs to a computer is still not clear.

How is the program to be communicated to the machine? First, we should say that the program is to be stored in the machine *before* the calculation begins. Present day computers, except for a few experimental projects, do not use voice input, so you cannot literally "tell" the machine what to do; however, we have mentioned some input methods. Many computers have a console typewriter on which it is possible to enter programs, but this is too slow unless there are many such typewriters—computers are expensive (tens of thousands to millions of dollars) and their time is valuable. Three commonly used methods are paper tape, magnetic tape, and punched cards; we will assume that our program is to be entered via punched cards.

Almost everyone has seen the punched cards widely used in business applications. The standard card, often called an IBM card regardless of manufacturer, has eighty columns, and each column can have a punch or series of punches standing for a letter, a number, or a special symbol. The details of the symbol coding will not concern us; it varies somewhat from machine to machine. When FORTRAN is used, each statement in the program usually occupies one card, although continuation cards are possible, as we have noted. Later in the chapter we shall discuss the proper location on the card for the FORTRAN statement.

Punching is usually done on a keypunch, a typewriter-like keyboard coupled with a mechanism which transports the cards. It may or may not print the character punched at the top of the column; if it does, this is for human convenience, since the computer is affected only by the punched slots. The card reader of the IBM 1620 can read 250 cards per minute, transferring the contents of each card to its memory. Punched cards are also used in other machines besides computers.

Here, however, we make a serious confession. Our computer does not understand FORTRAN! Each computer has its own language, called machine language, which it *does* understand, and every program to be executed must be in machine language. A machine language program looks very different from a FORTRAN program; it is a string of numbers. One instruction in the IBM 1620 machine language, for example, would usually have twelve numbers, the first two specifying an operation the computer is to carry out and the next ten, arranged in two groups of five each, specifying addresses in memory or other information. A few years ago all computer programs were written in machine language, so a program for one computer was very different from a program for the same calculation for another computer. Even today most computers have unique machine languages; for example, the language used by the IBM 1620 is unlike that used by the IBM 7094 or the CDC 3600. Recently, however, there has been some trend toward using the same machine language in different computers.

How are we to translate our FORTRAN program into a machine language program? The problem is similar to that of translating from English to French, except that our two languages, FORTRAN and one particular machine language, are simpler and have a more carefully defined grammatical structure than do natural languages. Unless such translation were possible, FORTRAN would not be a useful language. The trick is that the computer itself does the translation. Using a special computer program called the FORTRAN *compiler* program, it takes FORTRAN statements and translates them into strings of machine language instructions for the desired computation. We shall not outline how a compiler works, but for those interested, a good introductory discussion, based on a simplified language, is given in *Algorithms Computation and Mathematics*, revised edition. New Haven: School Mathematics Study Group, 1966.

To view the "translation" process, consider the following typical compilation, realizing that the details differ from machine to machine. Assume that the FORTRAN program is on cards. First, the FORTRAN compiler program is loaded into the core memory; in a small system the compiler might be on cards or paper tape, and entered from the appropriate input device, but in larger systems the compiler may be on magnetic tape, drum, or disk file. Then the user's program is put into the card reader. As the cards are read the translation process is begun; the FORTRAN cards can be considered as the data cards for the compiler program. With some compilers all translation is done as each FORTRAN statement is read (*one-pass compilation*), but it is more common to do the translation in a series of steps, perhaps translating first into an "intermediate language" and then to machine language. During compilation translated material may need to be stored outside the core memory, and the machine-language program may need to be loaded into memory before it is executed. Often the entire process is under the control of another manufacturer-supplied program, the monitor, supervisor, or operating system. When this is done the FORTRAN compiler is called into core memory by one or more control cards which precede the program.

FORTRAN was initially developed by IBM in connection with the 704 computer around 1957, but today it is available on almost every computer. The preparation of a FORTRAN compiler, a very complex program, is part of the work of developing a new computer. Although FORTRAN is only a few years old, it is used by tens of thousands of people, as it is now the most common scientific programming language. It is aimed particularly at scientific users, and perhaps its main characteristic is that it allows algebraic expressions in the program. But this is only one of the programming languages available today; such languages as ALGOL, MAD, JOVIAL, COBOL, COMIT, SNOBOL, LISP, IPL, JOSS, and many others are also used. And other languages, such as the new PL/1, are coming into use.

Some of these languages, particularly ALGOL and MAD, are algebraic languages which, like FORTRAN, are for calculational use. But others are oriented to different uses. COBOL is a business-oriented language, useful in maintaining large computer-stored files, keeping accounting records, billing, etc. Other languages are intended for the manipulation of strings of symbols; IPL-V was developed to enable the computer to imitate such human problem-solving activities as theorem-proving and to play complex games such as chess.

There may be more and more specialized languages developed for users with particular backgrounds. Thus there may be a future language for sociologists, another language for political scientists, etc. On the other hand, more powerful general-purpose languages are also under development; PL/1 combines features of algebraic, business, and list-processing languages.

Because of the linguistic aspects of computer languages, the tools of formal linguistics have been useful, particularly in problems of translation. ALGOL was initially specified by a complete formal syntax of the language. Thus the linguist has played an increasingly important role in computer development.

We have described FORTRAN as a single language. But this is far from the case; it is a family of related languages and dialects of an idealized FORTRAN language. Revised forms of FORTRAN have "evolved" from earlier forms. The three broad subdivisions at present are FORTRAN, FORTRAN II, and FORTRAN IV. FORTRAN IV, for example, usually allows logical variables, which take the values "true" or "false," in addition to numerical variables, and it also permits complex numbers. So far we have used only FORTRAN, but the use of indexed variables and subprograms in the three-body problem discussed in Chapter 6 is characteristic of FORTRAN II. In addition, the FORTRAN variation used differs from computer to computer, and different forms of FORTRAN may be available on the same computer. IBM has released at least four FORTRAN compilers for the 1620 computer, and numerous modifications of these have been made by IBM and by individual users. Some modifications attempt to match the characteristics of a particular computer, others are constructed for computational reasons. The standard operating system supplied with the large-scale IBM 7094 computer system contains *both* a FORTRAN II and a FORTRAN IV compiler.

Because of the multiplicity of FORTRAN, the final reference on the language must be the reference manual for the particular computer you are using; no one book can cover all the changing variants of FORTRAN.

A BRIEF SUMMARY OF ESSENTIAL FORTRAN

We have by no means made a detailed study of FORTRAN, but we have looked enough at FORTRAN statements to enable you to start writing simple programs. Here we summarize and slightly extend our discussion of the language in a form more convenient for reference, giving a brief, informal and far from complete, grammar of the FORTRAN language.

Numbers and variables

FORTRAN programs use two forms of numbers and variables, fixed point and floating point. Allowable ranges in size for both forms differ from compiler to compiler. Fixed-point numbers and the associated variables contain no decimal point, i.e., they are purely counting numbers or integers. Some recent FORTRAN literature uses the name "integer" instead of fixed point. A fixed-point variable is so designated by making the *first* letter of the variable an I, J, K, L, M, or N.

Floating-point variables (also called *real variables*) contain a decimal point. Two basic forms for floating-point numbers are employed in FORTRAN. The first form is with an explicit decimal point; the other is the FORTRAN equivalent to the scientific power-of-ten notation, which represents numbers of the form $X \times 10^Y$. Since a linear language like FORTRAN cannot use exponents explicitly, a special notation is needed for "10 to the power of." The notation adopted is the letter E. Thus the number 4.3×10^{17} is written in FORTRAN as 4.3E17. Floating-point variables can begin with any letter except those mentioned above for fixed-point variables. Floating-point numbers are stored in memory as two numbers; for example, in a number having the form $X \times 10^Y$ both X and Y are stored.

Variable names must begin with a letter. In many varieties of FORTRAN five or six letters or numbers are allowed in a name.

Arithmetic statements

An arithmetic statement is the FORTRAN way of representing an algebraic formula. The left-hand side consists of a single variable, which is separated from the right-hand side by an equal sign. The right-hand side can be any algebraic expression.

Algebraic expressions involve the operations of addition (+), subtraction (−), multiplication (*), division (/) and exponentiation (**).

Explicit functions in the FORTRAN library can also occur within algebraic statements. These usually include SINF, COSF, LOGF, EXPF, and SQRTF. The "F" at the end of these names is absent in many versions of FORTRAN IV. (Check the individual computer library for information regarding which functions are available.)

All the variables and constants on the right-hand side of an arithmetic expression must be in the same form; they must all be either fixed- or floating-point numbers or variables, except that floating-point numbers or variables may have fixed-point exponents. (Some FORTRAN languages allow *mixed-mode* expressions, but this usually increases computational time.)

Parentheses can be freely used within FORTRAN statements and should be used whenever any question as to the precise meaning of the statement might arise. (There is an assumed "order" to operations if parentheses are omitted, but this will not be discussed here.) Spaces can be used almost anywhere within a program where they are needed for clarity. (Many FORTRAN compilers eliminate spaces before translation, except those in an H-field in a FORMAT statement.)

Unconditional branching statement; GO TO

The unconditional branching statement is of the form

$$GO\ TO\ N$$

where N is the number of some other statement in the program. It transfers control to statement N in the program, breaking the linear sequence of commands. As with the conditional branch, the next statement after a GO TO is not accessible to the program unless it is a numbered statement and unless some other transfer statement refers to it. A "computed GO TO" statement in many FORTRAN variations produces a conditional branch.

Conditional transfer statement; arithmetic IF

The arithmetic IF statement assumes the form

$$IF\ (A)\ n,\ m,\ p$$

where *A* is an arithmetic expression, i.e., any numerical expression that could serve as the right-hand side of an arithmetic statement. The computer evaluates this expression. There are three possible actions which may be generated by the IF statement, depending on whether this expression is negative, zero, or positive, in that order. These cases correspond to the three statement numbers n, m, and p, which follow the expression in parentheses (commas separate the statement numbers). If the expression is negative, the control is transferred to the first statement number. If the value within the parentheses is zero, control is transferred to the statement having the second statement number. If the expression is positive, control is transferred to the statement with the third number. These numbers need not all be different, but they must correspond to existing statement numbers.

IF SENSE SWITCH

A conditional branching statement of the form

IF (SENSE SWITCH Q) n, m

where Q is an integer and n and m are statement numbers, refers to switches on the computer console. If switch number Q is on, control goes to the statement numbered n; if not, control goes to m. Since many computers do not have sense switches, this statement is not available with some FORTRAN compilers.

Input-output statements

Input-output statements instruct the computer either to accept a number and store it in memory or to reveal (print or punch) a number stored in memory. ACCEPT refers to information entered from the console. TYPE generates output on the typewriter, PRINT usually refers to the line printer, READ is for card input, and PUNCH produces output at the card punch. In each case the word is followed by a statement number, the number of a FORMAT statement somewhere else in the program. (With most compilers, FORMAT statements need not occur at any particular place in the program.) The FORMAT statement number is followed by a comma and a list of one or more variables to be entered or sent to output; the variables in the list are separated by commas.

The input-output statements of some variants of FORTRAN have a different structure. Only the words READ and WRITE are used, but the input or output device is indicated in the statement. The possible devices in an installation are assigned numbers; for example, 3 might be the symbol for the line printer. An output statement might be

WRITE (3, 7) A, B

The 7 refers to a FORMAT statement, while the 3 indicates that the values of A and B currently in memory are to be *printed*. Variables can be used for the device symbols. Thus if one wanted to choose the form of output (say, line printer or card punch) each time the program is run, one might use a statement like this:

WRITE (IOUT, 7) A, B

Other statements could allow the value of IOUT to be entered from the console before this statement is executed.

FORMAT statements

A FORMAT statement has a statement number, referred to in at least one input or output statement. Following the word "FORMAT" in the statement are a pair of parentheses. The material inside the parentheses describes the data structure. Different data descriptions within the parentheses are separated by a comma, the order corresponding to the order of the list in the input-output statement referring to the FORMAT statement. Data items may take any of the following forms:

1 *Alphanumeric data.* The letter H, preceded by the number of figures to be typed out, and followed by the letters and numbers themselves, indicates alphanumeric input or output. With some systems a comma after this specification is not required. Some recent compilers allow the use of "quotes" to designate such data.

2 The standard floating-point decimal output is of the form FA.B, where A gives the entire length of a number, including decimal point and sign, and B specifies the number of figures to the right of the decimal point. The number is assumed to be right-justified. If a datum contains a decimal point upon input, the F-specification is overridden.

3 The standard format specification for integers is IK, where K is an integer specifying the number of places needed.

4 Power-of-ten notation can be requested by a data specification of the form EA.B, where A and B have meanings which are similar to their F-format meanings. Many compilers do not require a comma after this specification.

5 The specification BX where B is a number, refers to B blank spaces. Many compilers do not require a comma after this specification.

Other specifications may also be available.

Halt Commands

PAUSE causes the computer to stop within the program and not execute the next instruction; pushing the start button transfers control to the command following the PAUSE statement. STOP also puts the computer in the manual mode, but now pressing the START button transfers control completely out of the program and into the next program, if the computer is operating under monitor control. CALL EXIT performs the same function as STOP except that it is not necessary to push the START button; it is usually available only if there is a monitor or operating system. Again these "rules" may not hold for a particular FORTRAN variant.

Card format for FORTRAN

Although some compilers ignore the manner in which FORTRAN statements are placed on the card, the following is the standard convention.

COLUMN 1   This column is reserved for a "C," signifying a comment statement which is to be ignored by the compiler.

COLUMNS 2 to 5   The statement number, if any. It does not need to be right or left justified. Some compilers allow the use of column one also for the statement number.

COLUMN 6   The continuation column. Normally it is blank, but if the statement is continued from a preceding card, column six is punched with any nonzero character.

COLUMNS 7 to 72   The FORTRAN statement. (Sometimes column 73 is also used.)

COLUMNS 73 to 80   These columns are reserved for identification or sequential numbering.

Problem 15. Find a physics text which discusses the "physical pendulum," a pendulum whose motion is not restricted to small angles, and write a FORTRAN program to solve the Newtonian differential equation for this system. What is the relation between this system and the harmonic oscillator? How do you expect the results to differ from those obtained from the harmonic oscillator calculation?

CHAPTER 6

THE THREE-BODY PROBLEM

So far we have been concerned with the mechanics of a single body. Feynman suggests at the end of his chapter that the same procedures can be carried over to problems involving more than one body, and outlines the solution for an *n*-body gravitational problem. This problem is particularly interesting, because the *n*-body problem, for *n* greater than two, has never been solved exactly, unlike the one- and two-body problems which have known exact analytic solutions. Hence, numerical techniques are not just a pedagogical convenience for the solution of problems involving three or more bodies; they are a necessity. We shall also introduce more of the resources of FORTRAN in connection with this problem. You may want to review Feynman, although our discussion will be self-contained.

We shall restrict ourselves to the gravitational force between three bodies. You can think of the three bodies as the earth, the moon, and a moon rocket fired from the earth for a landing on the moon. Or, the bodies might be the earth, the moon, and the sun. The rocket case is perhaps more interesting, since we have control over the motion of the third body.

The force is still the gravitational force; if we consider any two of the bodies, the force each exerts on the other is directed along the line connecting the two particles, and is directly proportional to the product of the masses of the particles and inversely proportional to the square of the distance between the two particles. You may have noticed the implicit assumption that this force is not affected by the presence of the third body. Or, in other words, each body exerts its force on each of the other bodies as though no other bodies were present, and the total force on one body is the vector sum of the individual forces due to the other two bodies. This is not a logical necessity but an assumption that "works"; that is, it gives results which experience has shown are accurate. It seems possible that when both bodies together act on a third body, the force might be some function of the individual forces more complicated than the sum. However, the sum gives experimentally verified results.

The immediate problem is to write this information, not in this verbal form but in an algebraic statement suitable for computation. If we are to compute the motion of one of the particles using numerical methods like those in Feynman, we must have analytic expressions for the force. Thus we must translate this information from the English language into the language of mathematics. We have had some practice at this already, but there are new difficulties here which we have not previously encountered.

In our previous problems, involving only a single particle, the position variable did not specify the particle. However, we must now describe the positions of three particles, so we need three different, distinguishable ways of designating position. Each of these positions is a triplicate of numbers. Since it would not be safe to assume, as we have previously assumed, that the motion takes place in a plane, we require three dimensions. Thus there will be nine position coordinates—three particles and three dimensions for each. As a result, the complexity of the problem and the amount of calculation will be greater than with single particle gravitational motion.

To represent three-dimensional motion as opposed to two-dimensional motion we can use the value "3" for a subscript on the variable in addition to "1" and "2". But we must also introduce some convention to designate the particle. We could give the particles names, using different coordinate terminology for each; however, it is reasonable to arrange our notation in as symmetrical and as elegant a fashion as possible. Thus, instead of assigning names of a literal type, we use number names, designating the particles as one, two, and three. We need to "attach" these ones, twos, and threes to the positions and velocities of the appropriate bodies in some distinguishable way. We could make them superscripts following the letter, and use parentheses to remind us that these superscripts are not powers. Thus the coordinates of the first particle might be

$$x_1^{(1)}, x_2^{(1)}, x_3^{(1)};$$

the coordinates of the second particle,

$$x_1^{(2)}, x_2^{(2)}, x_3^{(2)};$$

and the coordinates of the third particle,

$$x_1^{(3)}, x_2^{(3)}, x_3^{(3)}.$$

The advantage to this type of notation is that we can now use both subscripts and superscripts as variables. Thus when we write $x_i^{(j)}$, we refer to the ith component of the jth particle. Here i can take the values 1, 2, and 3 for the three components, and j is 1, 2, or 3, depending on which of the three particles is involved.

There are some obvious variants on this notation. We could use two subscripts, letting x_{ij} represent the ith component of the force on the jth particle; or both could be superscripts. Or we could number all nine of the position coordinates consecutively, letting the components (x_1, x_2, x_3) refer to the first particle, (x_4, x_5, x_6) refer to the second, and (x_7, x_8, x_9), to the third. We do not have any simple prescription which tells us in advance which notation is best. Rather, we can only make a heuristic judgment, an intelligent guess, as to which will be most useful, perhaps experimenting with several before committing ourselves.

Since all three of the particles will be moving with respect to each other, we no longer have any "natural" choice for the origin of the coordinates; thus we have not attempted to associate the coordinate system with any one particle. In general, in mechanics it is incorrect to fix the coordinate system to a particle; in fact, if we do this, we will often obtain a wrong prediction of the motion of the three bodies. This raises an issue which, although it has not been present and we will not describe it in detail, should be mentioned. We first arbitrarily set up a coordinate system to describe a motion; then we write the Newtonian laws of motion with quantities referring to that particular coordinate system. At this point we might suspect that there are possible limitations on this, and we would be correct in our assumption. There are only *certain* coordinate systems for which the laws of motion hold in the *usual* form. These acceptable coordinate systems for the Newtonian laws of motion are called *inertial systems*; if we *had* attached the coordinate system to one of the particles, the coordinate system would not have been inertial.

THE EQUATIONS OF MOTION

Let us determine the equations of motion for particle 1. First we need to determine the three components of the total force that is acting on this particle. We designate the three masses by $m^{(1)}$, $m^{(2)}$, and $m^{(3)}$. These components will be a sum of the contributions from particles 2 and 3. We first represent the gravitational force on particle 1 due to particle 2, knowing that the force is directed on the line between the two and knowing that it varies inversely as the square of the distance between them. Furthermore, we use the Newtonian assumption that this force is proportional to each of the masses. It is relatively easy to determine from Fig. 6–1 the distance between the particles. We have drawn the diagram in two dimensions, but using the Pythagorean theorem in a three-dimensional situation involves only

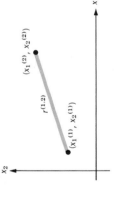

Figure 6-1

a simple change. Thus the distance between particle 1 and particle 2 is

$$r^{(1,2)} = \sqrt{(x_1^{(2)} - x_1^{(1)})^2 + (x_2^{(2)} - x_2^{(1)})^2 + (x_3^{(2)} - x_3^{(1)})^2}.$$

We see from the diagram that the difference in the two position vectors is directed along the line joining the two particles. The first component of the force on particle 1 due to the gravitational attraction of particle 2 only is

$$\frac{m^{(1)} m^{(2)} (x_1^{(1)} - x_1^{(2)})}{(r^{(1,2)})^3} = \frac{m^{(1)} m^{(2)} (x_1^{(1)} - x_1^{(2)})}{\left(\sqrt{(x_1^{(2)} - x_1^{(1)})^2 + (x_2^{(2)} - x_2^{(1)})^2 + (x_3^{(2)} - x_3^{(1)})^2}\right)^3}.$$

Like expressions give the force of particle 3 on particle 1. Hence, all we need to do is replace the "2" superscripts in the above expression by "3" superscripts. We can write the three components of the force due to *both* particles 2 and 3 acting on particle 1 as follows:

$$F_1^{(1)} = \frac{m^{(1)} m^{(2)} (x_1^{(1)} - x_1^{(2)})}{(r^{(1,2)})^3} + \frac{m^{(1)} m^{(3)} (x_1^{(1)} - x_1^{(3)})}{(r^{(1,3)})^3},$$

$$F_2^{(1)} = \frac{m^{(1)} m^{(2)} (x_2^{(1)} - x_2^{(2)})}{(r^{(1,2)})^3} + \frac{m^{(1)} m^{(3)} (x_2^{(1)} - x_2^{(3)})}{(r^{(1,3)})^3},$$

$$F_3^{(1)} = \frac{m^{(1)} m^{(2)} (x_3^{(1)} - x_3^{(2)})}{(r^{(1,2)})^3} + \frac{m^{(1)} m^{(3)} (x_3^{(1)} - x_3^{(3)})}{(r^{(1,3)})^3}.$$

Or, equivalently, all three components of force can be written in a more compact form using a variable index:

$$F_i^{(1)} = \frac{m^{(1)} m^{(2)} (x_i^{(1)} - x_i^{(2)})}{(r^{(1,2)})^3} + \frac{m^{(1)} m^{(3)} (x_i^{(1)} - x_i^{(3)})}{(r^{(1,3)})^3}, \qquad i = 1, 2, \text{ or } 3.$$

We can similarly write the forces on particle 2 and on particle 3.

It might seem that we could ignore these other components and discuss only the motion of particle 1. But the three particles are interacting and their positions are constantly changing. Hence we should not determine the motion of only one particle but must consider the entire system of three particles as a unit. Each time we increase the time by Δt we must find the new positions and the new velocities for *all* three particles.

We have many basic equations to consider. For each particle there are three equations which determine the new positions. We can write these nine equations in a very brief form in component notation as follows:

$$x_i^{(j)\prime} = x_i^{(j)} + \Delta t \cdot v_i^{(j)}; \qquad i = 1, 2, 3; \quad j = 1, 2, 3.$$

The prime is used to indicate the new position coordinate. The notation for the nine velocity components "matches" that for the position components. Similarly, there are nine equations which determine the new velocities. It is a little less convenient to write these equations in abbreviated form because of the complex expressions for the components of force. If we use the notation for the forces just introduced rather than the explicit expressions, we can write the following velocity equations:

$$v_i^{(j)} = v_i^{(j)} + F_i^{(j)} \cdot \Delta t / m^{(j)}; \qquad i = 1, 2, 3; \quad j = 1, 2, 3.$$

Note that the $m^{(j)}$ here cancels with the $m^{(j)}$ in $F_i^{(j)}$, so the calculation for the jth particle does not use the mass of that particle.

Eventually we must use all 18 equations, as compared to four in the single-body problem. We have a large calculation on our hands if we expect to find how three particles with specified initial conditions move under mutual gravitational forces, particularly if we consider the complicated nature of the force expressions.

FORTRAN ARRAYS AND DO LOOPS

In this situation, there is today almost no point in considering the calculation unless we consider it as a computer problem, although many such problems were laboriously solved before the days of computers. We assume that our desired programming language is FORTRAN. The program could be written with what we presently know about FORTRAN, but this would be long and wasteful. Hence we shall use this calculation to learn more of FORTRAN facilities.

Position and velocity are each described by nine quantities; however, these nine quantities are classifiable in a simple way. There are three particles and for each particle there are three components for position and velocity. We have been designating these quantities with subscripts and superscripts. There are many situations in physics and the other sciences in which variables occur in sets of this kind, so it is not surprising that FORTRAN has the capability to work with them.

Consider the nine components of position. In FORTRAN we designate an arbitrary component by

$$X(I,J)$$

Here I and J are both fixed-point (integer) variables which assume the values 1, 2, and 3. We shall (arbitrarily) use the first of these two subscripts, I in the above expression, for the component of position, and the second, J, for the particle. Hence X(2,3) refers to the second component of the position of particle 3. A variable of this kind, with subscripts or indices, is called an array in FORTRAN; one, two, or three indices are usually allowed.

Arrays in FORTRAN programs present new problems for the translating program; the compiler needs to know how much storage to allocate to a dimensioned variable. In FORTRAN, as opposed to some more recent and sophisticated algebraic languages, storage requirements are specified in advance and cannot be changed during execution of the program. Unless the program is told the ranges over which the subscripts vary, it has no way of knowing how much storage to allocate. This leads to a new type of statement, the DIMENSION statement. To specify that the position variable has a range of three in each of its two indices, one writes a FORTRAN dimension statement as follows:

DIMENSION X(3,3)

Dimension statements must occur in the program *before* the variables to which they refer are used; some compilers require that they precede any executable statement. Any number of variables may be "dimensioned" in one statement, the variables being separated by a comma.

There is another type of FORTRAN statement which is of great use with subscripted variables, and is also usable in other situations. The DO statement is not an "essential" part of the language, in that what it does can be accomplished with IF and arithmetic statements, but it allows convenient manipulation of subscripted quantities and, for this reason, it is a powerful statement. The DO statement in FORTRAN can be characterized by the following examples:

DO 100 L = 1, 3

DO 56 L = 1, N

DO 97 KIP = 4, 11, 2

A statement number always follows the word DO, and it is the number of a statement that occurs somewhere in the program *after* the DO statement; in the first example this is statement 100. The statement with this number is the terminating sentence of the DO "loop." The DO statement operates as follows: When the DO statement is first encountered, the fixed-point variable in it (L in the first example above) is set equal to the initial fixed-point value listed (1 in the first example). This initial value has to be one or greater than one. Then the program continues until the numbered statement which terminates the loop is encountered. At that point the DO variable is increased by 1 (usually—see below) and control returns to the statement following the DO statement. The program keeps going through the loop until the variable is greater than the *second* value designated, at which point control is directed to the statement following the DO loop terminating statement.

As you can see in the examples, the first and second values can be fixed-point constants or variables which are assigned values during the execution of the program before the DO loop is entered. The third example shows another possibility; when three variables or constants occur after the equal sign, the third designates how much the variable increases each time the loop begins again. Thus in the third example KIP has the successive values 4, 6, 8, and 10. If there is no third variable, the increment is assumed to be 1.

There are grammatical rules for DO loops. First, it is not permitted to transfer from outside the loop to a sentence within the DO loop by the use of a branching statement. Each time the loop is entered it should be entered at the beginning. On the other hand, it is perfectly satisfactory to transfer out of a DO loop at any time with an IF or GO statement.

Second, DO loops can be nested, but these nests must be overlapping rather than intersecting. Thus if one DO loop begins inside another DO loop, the inner DO loop cannot end at a statement coming *after the end* of the first DO loop. This is easy to see in a diagram usually presented in discussions of FORTRAN; Fig. 6–2 shows allowable and nonallowable possibilities. The brackets show the range of the DO loops.

Many compilers will not accept all FORTRAN statements as final DO-loop statements. A "do-nothing" statement, CONTINUE, is often used to terminate a DO loop.

WRITING THE PROGRAM

We now have enough information to begin to write our program. We expect this program to be more complex than the earlier ones. It is reasonable to write complicated programs in pieces, since we tend to think of *calculation* as a series of stages. Also, if troubles develop, it is easier to find them when we can test each section separately.

Perhaps the first problem is computing the nine force components; we must find the Jth component of the force on the Kth particle, where J and K each go over the range 1, 2, and 3. Each time we want to find the force on one of the particles, we need to determine the distances to the two other particles. We could compute these before determining each component of the force on each particle. But this would be wasteful; it involves eighteen separate calculations of distances, while at

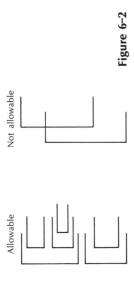

Allowable

Not allowable

Figure 6–2

any time there are only *three* distances between the three particles. So our strategy will be to find all the distances at a given time before computing any of the forces at that time. Using an obvious notation, R(L,M) denotes the distance between the Lth and Mth particles. Note that R(L,M) = R(M,L), and that R(L,L) = 0 (this is not needed in the calculation, fortunately), so it is necessary to compute only the values for which L < M.

In the following program for determining distances we have designated R2 as a temporary storage location for the square of the distance.

```
        DO 200  M = 1, 3
        DO 200  L = 1, 3
        IF (L-M) 600, 200, 200
600     R2 = 0.
        DO 100  N = 1, 3
        R2 = R2 + (X(N,L) − X(N,M)) * (X(N,L) − X(N,M))
100     CONTINUE
        R(L,M) = SQRTF(R2)
        R(M,L) = R(L,M)
200     CONTINUE
```

This is certainly not a self-contained program; it assumes that the values of the position, X(I,J), have been made available in memory prior to this part of the calculation. We calculate the distance by Pythagorean methods in the DO 100 loop. We set R2 equal to zero before entering this loop and then add three successive squares of the differences between the position coordinates for the Lth and Mth particles. The IF statement assures us that we will only make three calculations for the three distances, although we go through the big (outer) DO loops nine (3 × 3) times. The purpose of the two CONTINUE statements is merely to show the ends of the DO loops. Note that we obtain the square of a number by multiplying the number by itself; this usually involves fewer machine instructions than raising to the second power.

The calculation of the distance is preliminary to determining the forces. We are **not** concerned with the force on the Kth particle, but the force *per unit mass* on the Kth particle. Because the gravitational force contains the same mass, and because the equations of motion contain the same mass, the equations for calculating the new velocities will not contain the mass of the particle for which this calculation is made, but it *will* contain the masses of the other two particles.

We can now write the program for the force on the Kth particle due to the Jth particle as shown in Fig. 6–3.

Note that there is a slight modification in the distance part of the calculation. The previous coding calculated the three distances, each of which could be cubed

```
      FUNCTION FORCE(I,J)
      DIMENSION R3(3,3), X(3,3), AM(3)
      COMMON X, AM
C     FORCE(I,J) IS THE ITH COMPONENT OF FORCE FOR THE JTH PARTICLE
C     PER UNIT MASS
      DO 200 L = 1, 3
      IF (I + J − 2) 800, 800, 700
800   DO 200 M = 1, 3
      IF (L − M) 600, 200, 200
600   R = 0.
      DO 100 N = 1, 3
      R = R + (X(N,L) − X(N,M)) * (X(N,L) − X(N,M))
100   CONTINUE
      R3(L,M) = R ** 1.5
      R3(M,L) = R3(L,M)
200   CONTINUE
C     R3(L,M) IS THE CUBE OF THE DISTANCE BETWEEN THE LTH AND MTH
C     PARTICLE
700   F = 0.
      DO 300 L = 1, 3
      IF (L − J) 400, 300, 400
400   F = F + AM(L) * (X(I,L) − X(I,J)) / R3(L,J)
300   CONTINUE
      FORCE = F
      RETURN
      END
```

Figure 6-3

when needed. Since each force component involves a contribution from each of the other two particles, then each force component uses two distance numbers, and there are three components of the force for each of the three particles. Thus we would be cubing eighteen numbers, but only *three* are distinct! Hence there will be a considerable saving of calculating time if we do this cubing initially for each distance. Therefore, instead of taking the square root, the statement following 200 now raises the quantity to the power of 3/2.

The force is designated by F or FORCE and is computed in the DO 300 loop. Before this loop is entered F is set to zero. In the loop a term is computed for the values of L other than J and it is added to the other terms. You can see that this term is simply the expression for the force on the Jth particle due to the Lth particle. Thus it is not surprising that we obtain the total force if we sum over the possible values of L except L = J. The IF statement branches around this unwanted value.

You will note that, as in the preceding program, the DO loop is ended by the dummy CONTINUE statement, which produces no action in the FORTRAN program. It is not necessarily needed; with most FORTRAN compilers one could drop it and change the statement to read DO 400, rather than DO 300. However, most experienced programmers feel that there is an advantage in ending DO loops with CONTINUE statements, even if it is not absolutely required. If there are corrections to be made, such as the insertion of other statements or variables within the DO loop, the card with the CONTINUE statement can always be moved to the new end of the DO loop caused by the corrections. This often saves some work.

But how are we to use this piece of the program in the entire program? Each time we start to use the approximations to the Newtonian equations of motion, we need forces. This program calculates the forces. Several possibilities are available; for instance, we could simply put this whole program before the equations of motion in our program. This follows more or less the practice of previous programs.

However, with FORTRAN II and FORTRAN IV there is another method promising greater versatility that will allow us to handle this program as a separate piece of the full program. We can make this program piece into a subprogram that will be referenced in the main program. There are several ways of doing this in FORTRAN. A convenient method for our needs here is a *function subprogram*.

There are only a few statements in this program that have not already been mentioned. The first statement, FUNCTION FORCE (I,J), identifies the program as a function subprogram. The function has the name FORCE assigned to it and it is specified as having two subscripts whose values are to come from the main program. This function is available as a function in the FORTRAN program; thus we can use it directly in arithmetic statements and treat it just as we do the square root or cosine functions. Each time an arithmetic statement that contains this new function is executed, the program branches to this function subprogram, bringing with it the values of the two indices I and J from the main program. Note that the next to the last statement in the subprogram tells us that the calculated F is to be the force. This value is then "returned," as the last statement indicates, to the main program, as is the flow of control.

The one other new idea in the program is in the third statement, COMMON X, AM. This sentence has to do with the problems of communication between a main program and its subprogram. In order to calculate the force the program must have accessible to it the values of the positions and the masses of the three particles. The positions have presumably been calculated in a previous stage of the main program, and they are stored somewhere in a region determined by that program. But when the subprogram is called, it must know where the main program has stored these values. We can ensure that the locations will be available to the subprogram by putting exactly the same COMMON statement in *both* the main program and the subprogram. These statements instruct the compiler to store the values of the variables X and AM in a place in the memory known as COMMON, a region accessible to all parts of the program. None of the other variables will be stored in this region. Furthermore, the order of their storage in COMMON is the order of their occurrence in the COMMON statement. Hence the names are not terribly important; if X and AM were consistently called Q and Z by the main program, but were always listed in the same order—the first one a doubly superscripted variable with each variable having a range of three and the second a singly subscripted variable with a range of three—then the storage would be in the same location in the COMMON area for both the main program and the subprogram.

COMMON is also useful when a FORTRAN program is too long to be run in one piece without exceeding the size of the core memory of the computer. In such a situation the program can, in some systems, be broken up into links. These successive links can be stored on disk or tape and called in when needed. The data from one link to be used in the next link can be stored in COMMON, since this area of memory is not altered when the new link of the program replaces the old link in the core memory. Note that the variables occurring in the COMMON statement have just occurred in a DIMENSION statement. It is not necessary to indicate in the COMMON statement the subscripts associated with these variables.

Since we have not discussed the main program, it is not clear why the first IF statement, which involves the values I and J, is needed. If both I and J are unity, the computer calculates the distances between the three particles, but if the

the three-body problem

```
      DIMENSION X(3,3), V(3,3), AM(3)
      COMMON X, AM
3000  PUNCH 305
305   FORMAT (32H THREE BODY GRAVITATIONAL MOTION   //)
      PRINT 306
306   FORMAT (35HSPECIFY THREE MASSES, 5 SPACES EACH )
      T = 0.
      DELT = .01
      ACCEPT 405, AM
405   FORMAT (3F5.3)
      DO 4000 I = 1, 3
      PRINT 505, I
505   FORMAT (53HENTER 3 POSITION AND VELOCITY COMPONENTS FOR
     1PARTICLE , I2, 15H, 5 SPACES EACH )
      ACCEPT 605, (X(J,I), J = 1, 3), (V(K,I), K = 1, 3)
605   FORMAT (6E5.2)
4000  CONTINUE
      PUNCH 606, X
606   FORMAT (17HINITIAL POSITIONS /(17X, 3F15.5))
      PUNCH 705, V
705   FORMAT (18HINITIAL VELOCITIES /(17X, 3F15.5))
      PUNCH 805, AM
805   FORMAT (6HMASSES , 10X, 3F12.5)
      PUNCH 115
115   FORMAT (/6H TIME ,33X, 22HCOMPONENTS OF POSITION  /)
      DO 5000 I = 1, 3
      DO 5000 J = 1, 3
      V(I,J) = V(I,J) + FORCE(I,J) * DELT / 2.
5000  CONTINUE
8000  DO 2000 K = 1, 10
      DO 1000 L = 1, 10
      DO 1000 I = 1, 3
      DO 1000 J = 1, 3
      X(I,J) = X(I,J) + V(I,J) * DELT
      V(I,J) = V(I,J) + FORCE(I,J) * DELT
1000  CONTINUE
      T = T + DELT * 10.
      PUNCH 105, T, X
105   FORMAT (F6.2/(10X, 3F15.6))
2000  CONTINUE
      PRINT 205, T
205   FORMAT (11HTIME IS NOW , F6.2 )
      IF (SENSE SWITCH 2) 6000, 8000
6000  IF (SENSE SWITCH 3) 7000, 3000
C     2 ON FOR NEW INITIAL CONDITIONS, 2 AND 3 ON TO EXIT
7000  CALL EXIT
      END
```

Figure 6—4

values of I and J are greater than unity, control is directed to the calculation of the forces. The strategy is as follows: I and J will be the variables in the DO loops in the calculation using the equations of motion in the main program. The first time these loops are entered for a given time, i.e., when F(1,1) is requested, the three distances are calculated. After that they are used for each of the succeeding eight passes through the loops without being recalculated.

We are now ready for the main program. It does not contain much that is new, but it does show some new methods for handling input and output of subscripted variables. The program for the main calculation is shown in Fig. 6–4.

Note that the COMMON statement is the same here as it is in the function subprogram, thus ensuring that both programs have access to these variables. Punching is assumed for the output. The resulting cards can be listed by an off-line printer, or could serve as input data for some other program.

The calculation of the new positions and velocities occurs in the two inner DO 1000 loops. The variables I and J, which index these loops, are the parameters used in calling the force function. The first arithmetic expression in the loops calculates the new position components and the second calculates the new velocity components. As we have discussed, the FORCE function is used directly in the expression for calculating the new velocity.

The program assumes that the time step DELT is 0.01; however, it also assumes that this is too often to punch the positions, so it punches only every tenth calculation. This is the work of the outer DO 1000 loop; the variable in this loop, L, is not used in the remainder of the program, but serves only as a counter, counting the ten times through the loop before punching. To make the output self-contained, initial conditions are also punched. It is also reassuring to know in a program like this how far computation has progressed, since the full information is not seen on the typewriter or line printer. Hence for every 100 calculations, for every tenth time information is punched, the typewriter or printer informs us how far along the calculation has advanced.

It remains for us to comment on the use of array variables in input and output statements in FORTRAN. The statement PUNCH 105, T, X gives an example of this. We know that X, the position, is a doubly subscripted variable, where the first variable indicates the component of the position and the second variable, the particle. But in this sentence we have listed it as X, without its subscripts. Under such conditions, *all* the values of the variable will be printed out. The FORTRAN compiler assumes that the order of input or output for a doubly-subscripted variable, otherwise unspecified, will be X(1,1), X(2,1), X(3,1), X(1,2), X(2,2), X(3,2), X(1,3), X(2,3), X(3,3). We want the first line to contain the time and the three position components for each of the three particles to occupy separate lines, as shown below:

```
· · ·              (time)
X₁, X₂, X₃         (first particle)
X₁, X₂, X₃         (second particle)
X₁, X₂, X₃         (third particle)
```

The FORMAT statement, 105, carries out our wishes. It generates four cards for each PUNCH statement which refers to it. The first card contains only the time and each of the next three cards has components for one of the three particles. The inner parentheses within the FORMAT statement ensure that the program goes to the left-hand inner parenthesis after each group of three to find specifications for the variables again, using a new card. Note that the slash (/) also calls for a new card.

Another situation is illustrated in the earlier ACCEPT 605 statement. Here we are entering from the typewriter the initial values of the position and the velocity for each of the particles. Since this is a collection of 18 numbers, it must be organized in some rational way. Our intention is to type six numbers on each line; the first three will be the position components and the next three, the velocity components for the same particle. The FORMAT statement, 605, refers to six variables. This statement occurs within the DO 4000 loop, where I takes on the values 1, 2, and 3, designating the particular particle involved. The first time through the loop, I is equal to 1, and in this case the ACCEPT statement refers to X(I,1) and V(K,1). In each of these cases J and K take the values 1, 2, and 3, and the ACCEPT statement tells us first to enter the three position components and then to type in three values of the velocity components, which is what is desired. Perhaps you have noted that the I and J are used both here and later; these two parts of the program do not overlap, so there is no possible confusion and we save a little storage space.

The ACCEPT 405 statement lists the subscripted variable AM, a variable with a single subscript, by giving its name but not its subscript. Again the assumption is that all the values are entered and that the order is that of the integers.

Problem 16. Alter the preceding program so that it solves a four-body gravitational problem. Make as few changes as possible in the existing program.

Problem 17. Alter the program so that it works for *n* bodies. Assume that *n* ≤ 10, and require that the number of particles be typed in at the beginning of the program. Note that, because the FORTRAN compiler allocates storage during compilation rather than during calculation, it is necessary to dimension all variables with their largest possible ranges.

Problem 18. The Euler method for solving this problem, the method used in Feynman, becomes very unstable for small values of the distances between the particles, because small errors in these distances become huge errors in $1/r^3$. Add a test which will check to see whether the distance is at least 0.2. The program should command the computer to type a message and stop if the distance between any two particles becomes less than 0.2.

Problem 19. How can this program be tested? Remember that a program which runs without any obvious error may *not* be doing what you intend it to do.

Problem 20. It is a difficult task to fully study the three-body problem, because the calculation is lengthy and there are so many possible choices for initial conditions and masses. A more tractable problem is that of the motion of a planet about a binary star system. The closest star to us, 2 Centauri, is a binary with masses 1.08 and 0.88 (our sun is the unit mass). The distance between the components can be assumed to be 20 A. U. (astronomical units—the mean distance from the sun to the earth is one A. U.). The system has a period of about 80 years, and the eccentricity of the orbits is about 0.5. If you have enough time available on a fast computer, investigate the motion of a planet about the earth's size in such a system. In connection with this problem, you may be interested in reading the discussion in *Habitable Planets for Man*, by S. H. Dole (New York: Blaisdell, 1964), particularly the material on pp. 76–80.

The reader may be interested in the following description of an early computer project similar to the one described in this chapter.

"One of the most celebrated classical problems of physical science is known as the 'three-body' problem. It is concerned with the motion of three bodies in space under the action of their mutual gravitational attractions. Traditionally, the three bodies have been the Sun, Earth, and Moon; nowadays they might be the Earth, the Moon, and an artificial satellite travelling through space between them. Since 1750 no less than 800 scientific papers, many of them bearing the names of the greatest mathematicians, have been published on this problem. The mathematical equations governing the motions are easy enough to write down, but they cannot be solved mathematically and their numerical solution is impractical by pencil-and-paper methods. Fortunately, however, for the development of astronomy, it was found possible to develop approximate methods to deal with most problems of practical interest. In the case of the solar system, for instance, the Sun exerts such a predominating gravitational effect that the motion of any planet can be computed with sufficient accuracy for practical purposes by assuming that each of the other planets exerts only a small perturbing effect on the basic elliptic orbit of the planet in question. There the matter rested until 1950, when Dr. W. J. Eckert and his colleagues, using one of the early IBM computers, solved not merely the 'three-body' problem, but a six-body problem. They calculated the position of the five major planets—Jupiter, Saturn, Uranus, Neptune, and Pluto—from A.D. 1653 to A.D. 2000 at intervals of forty days. The computations were based on some 25,000 observations, most of them between 1750 and 1940, and the planetary paths were calculated to fourteen decimal places—that is to say, more accurately than they can be observed. About twelve million operations were performed altogether. Each one had to be carefully checked as part of the program, because a single error would have invalidated the whole of the subsequent work. The published results, containing 1½ million figures, occupied a volume of 324 large pages. Many larger calculations have been done since, but to have carried through a task of this magnitude as early as 1950 was a notable achievement indeed."*

SUBPROGRAMS IN FORTRAN

The function subprogram is only one of several ways to use subprograms in FOR-TRAN. Here we consider briefly another variety of subprogram, the subroutine. It has a slightly different heading than a function subprogram, and it is "called" differently from the main program, but other details are similar. A typical first statement in a subroutine might be as follows:

SUBROUTINE NEWTON (X, Y, I)

The number of parameters is variable; it could be zero.

Control would be transferred from the main program to this subroutine by a main program statement of this type:

CALL NEWTON (P, Z * Z / 4, 3)

where P is a variable name in the main program. It may have a value in the main program which is "passed" to the subroutine through this call statement, or it may be a variable to be calculated in the subroutine and returned to the main program. Variables, arithmetic expressions, and constants can occur in the arguments of the CALL statement.

When executed, a FORTRAN subroutine typically has internal storage for its own variables, and the values (if any) which are known when the subroutine is entered are stored at these locations in memory. In the above example, 3 will be stored for I, and $Z^2/4$ (using the value of Z in the main program) for Y. Values calculated within the subroutine will also be stored internally by the subroutine, but if they are in the parameter list, such variables will be returned to the storage of the main program whenever a RETURN statement is encountered in the subroutine. Just as

*From S. H. Hollingdale and G. C. Tootill, *Electronic Computers* (Baltimore: Penguin Books, 1965). Reprinted by permission.

with function subroutines, there may be several RETURN statements in a subprogram. Program control returns to the statement following the CALL statement in the main program. The COMMON statement has the same effect as it does with function subprograms in that if it occurs in *both* the main program and the subprogram, then only *one* storage area will be assigned for the variables named in the statement. The variables in COMMON are accessible to both the main program and the subprogram.

Usually a function subprogram can return only a single value, but a subroutine can return several values.

In our FORCE subprogram for the three-body problem we used the same names for the variables in the main program that we used for the dummy arguments in the subprogram. This is acceptable if the system being used allows the two programs to be compiled separately. But if they are to be compiled together, it may be necessary to assign different names to the dummy arguments. In any case they should agree in number and type of variable. Thus if the subroutine has three actual arguments, the first a fixed-point variable, the second a floating-point variable, and the third a fixed-point variable, the three necessary dummy arguments in the CALL statement should be fixed, floating, and fixed, respectively. Advanced compilers may allow optional parameters.

DIFFERENTIAL EQUATIONS, NUMERICAL METHODS, AND ERRORS

The study of Newtonian mechanics leads to solving equations containing derivatives of the functions desired, i.e., differential equations. In this chapter we discuss briefly some aspects of the solution of differential equations.

First, some details already suggested deserve further emphasis. The solution to the familiar polynomial equation of elementary algebra is a number or a collection of numbers. But the differential equation is a different mathematical entity from a quadratic equation, since its solution is a *function*.

This is not complete. Given a quadratic equation, we are assured by the fundamental theorem of algebra that we can obtain two (possibly equal) unique roots. But a differential equation has no unique solution; rather it has an infinite family of solutions. In our programs we use *more* than the differential equation to specify the solution. At the beginning of Section 9–5 Feynman assumes initial values for the position and velocity of the harmonic oscillator for $t = 0$. For the numerical method these initial conditions are essential; the approximation equations tell how to find the new position and velocity, *given* the old position and velocity. One must begin somewhere in a bootstrap operation, so initial values of position and velocity are specified to start the calculation. For the two-dimensional gravitational problem, we require four numbers as initial conditions, the two position components and the two velocity components. Different initial conditions usually produce different solutions to the same differential equation.

Generally, a solution to a differential equation is uniquely determined only if auxiliary information is specified. Although we cannot prove the relevant theorems, we can make an intelligent guess as to how much information is needed, based on our experience with numerical methods and with Feynman's examples. We can view the harmonic oscillator equation as a single equation with a second derivative, a second-order equation,

$$d^2x/dt^2 = -x,$$

or as a pair of first-order equations,

$$dv/dt = -x \quad \text{and} \quad v = dx/dt.$$

The initial conditions on position and velocity give two numbers. Considered similarly, the gravitational problem is described by either two second-order equations or four first-order equations, and four initial conditions are needed. So we might conjecture that n constants are needed to determine uniquely the solution of n first-order differential equations, a conjecture which (with appropriate conditions) can be supported.

It is not essential that the constants be initial conditions, conditions for $t = 0$. In mechanical problems, for example, it is sufficient to specify the position at two different times to determine uniquely the motion, although the numerical methods used here are not suitable for such a problem. Some important formulations of mechanics do require such information. Or one could give the velocity at two times; the only important condition is the "two-ness," since a one-dimensional Newtonian problem corresponds to two first-order differential equations.

ERRORS

Even the inexperienced user of numerical methods needs some understanding of errors in calculations. Three basic types of errors occur in numerical procedures, and they present special problems with the computer. The first, *round-off error*, happens because the computer stores a number with a finite number of significant figures. In large scientific computers a "word" in storage might be as large as 64 binary bits. Even in machines with a variable word length any one number has only a limited number of places, binary or decimal. Thus in every case the number stored is finite, and in most computations the results are to an extent an approximation. For example, if one is divided by three in a decimal machine, the decimal-notation result stored must be terminated somewhere, and the "thrown-away" part of the nonending exact result is called a round-off error.

Round-off error may seem unimportant. For example, the 1620 FORTRAN program usually carries floating-point computations to eight significant decimal figures, more than most hand calculations, so the loss of the ninth and higher places may not appear significant. However, remember that the solution of a differential equation by numerical methods is an iterative process which involves many calculations. It is reasonable to expect round-off error to increase as the number of calculations increases. As the time steps become smaller, more calculations are needed to reach a given value of the time, and round-off error increases.

The second type of error is due to the numerical methods used. In solving differential equations, we replace the differential equation by a "difference" equation which can be solved by calculational techniques. This transition from the equation we want to solve to another equation which closely resembles it is the key to the approximation method for solving differential equations. Since we have tampered with the initial equation, we cannot expect the precise solution we want; our best hope is to get close. The error introduced by the approximation is called *truncation error*, due to the result being truncated before it had all the terms that might be used to express it.

One might guess that truncation error usually decreases as the step decreases. We replace a derivative by a ratio of differences, and we expect that for well-behaved functions the ratio of differences will be closer to the derivative when the time step Δt is relatively small. Precisely how truncation error depends on the time step is a question of the integration method used. For the simpler Euler method used here the truncation error is on the order of $(\Delta t)^2$.* However, *decreasing* Δt does not necessarily improve the accuracy of the calculation, because for small Δt round-off error becomes increasingly greater.

In a calculation by computer or by hand, round-off errors and truncation errors occur at each step. One practical possibility is to study the question empirically. For example, the harmonic oscillator program allows the time step to be entered as data each time the program is used, so experimentation with different time steps is possible. We could see how much the accuracy was affected by halving the time step. If this affected only the fourth or fifth place in the answer, we might feel that the time step was reasonable. But if cutting the step in half made a drastic difference, a smaller step might still be needed. Thus numerical experimentation, while not giving an absolute answer to the error problem, is sometimes a useful procedure.

Elaborate analyses of errors exist in the literature, but these are often impractical to use. One important question is how the error at one stage affects the next stage of the calculation. One can envision a bad possibility in which the errors are cumulative and perhaps even magnified in successive steps; a relatively small error at one step might be magnified in each step and so the solution obtained at each step might move farther and farther from the true solution. An error of this kind is called a *propagated error*.

Occasionally, the nature of the problem suggests an internal method to check on the accuracy of the calculation. For example, the law of areas might give some indication of the accuracy of central force calculations; the closure of the orbit might also be used as a measure of accuracy.

---

*J. M. McCormick and M. G. Salvadori, *Numerical Methods in FORTRAN* (Englewood Cliffs, N.J.: Prentice-Hall, 1964), p. 97.

NUMERICAL METHODS FOR SOLVING DIFFERENTIAL EQUATIONS

In this book we used one method of solving differential equations, Feynman's procedure of replacing the true velocity by the average velocity. This method, which can be viewed in ways other than replacing a derivative by a ratio of differences, is called the Euler method. It is perhaps the simplest numerical method available for differential equations; the literature is full of many much more complex numerical procedures for solving differential equations. One might wonder why more complex methods would be used instead of simpler methods, as they often are in practice. The main reason concerns error; these methods give, for a fixed time step, a closer approximation to the true solution. We shall not review these methods (the appendix lists appropriate references) but we must mention their existence.

Large computer centers often have programs in the library for solving differential equations, using sophisticated methods. The Scientific Subroutine Package for the IBM System 360 lists, for example, a program for solving up to six first-order differential equations using the Runge-Kutta method, a widely used method.

DIFFERENTIAL EQUATIONS AND ANALYTIC SOLUTIONS

At this point it will be well for us to consider what has been happening. The basic equations of classical mechanics are differential equations; not only do the position variables occur in the equations but their derivatives do also. Thus to solve problems of classical mechanics, to predict how bodies will move given forces, it is necessary to solve differential equations. In many other areas of physics the basic laws also lead to differential equations, so the situation is not unique to mechanics.

But it is wrong to assume that numerical methods are the only methods used, since they represent only one group of procedures for solving differential equations. Two broad classes should be distinguished. The one used here is an example of the first kind, the numerical approximation to the solution.

A second approach to solving differential equations, the analytic method, does not proceed by making approximations, but looks for exact descriptions of the functions that will satisfy the differential equation. Feynman's Eqs. 9.10 are an analytic solution of Eq. 9.9, just as the cosine function is an analytic solution for the harmonic oscillator problem. When analytic solutions can be obtained, they are desired. Analytic solutions are sought not only because they exhibit the solution in exact form rather than approximate form, but also because they have an elegance and simplicity that is missing in the long tables of numbers obtained by a numerical method. The physicist favors analytic methods when they can be used successfully. They have a crispness and a clearness numerical methods lack and they are often very powerful. Furthermore, they offer more thorough information. In the development of new areas of physics analytic methods are almost always essential.

Unfortunately, many problems cannot now be solved exactly. In these cases numerical methods are the only resort; analytic methods are not universally applicable, so many problems must be solved by numerical techniques. This is particularly true when the basic equations are very complex.

Our present case is somewhat peculiar. The problems we have studied have known analytic solutions, except for the three-body problem. We used numerical techniques for a different reason. The analytic methods require more time to learn and more mathematical understanding than do numerical methods. The advantage of numerical methods is that they allow the student with limited mathematical background to approach the basic problem in all physics, the solution of a differential equation. If you continue in physics it is very likely that you will learn to solve problems such as the gravitational problem by analytic methods; the physicist needs to know a variety of different methods, so that he can choose the most appropriate one for the problem at hand.

Some complex problems are best solved by a combination of exact and approximate methods, and imaginative use of the computer is proving to be advantageous for such problems.

MORE ON PROGRAMMING

ALGORITHMIC VERSUS HEURISTIC PROGRAMS

We might distinguish three stages in writing computer programs. We first begin with a physical problem. Understanding this problem and determining how to translate a verbal statement of the problem into a precise mathematical statement often affords much of the difficulty in problem solving. Students at all levels have difficulty applying mathematical techniques to a nontrivial English language problem. This translation constitutes the first stage in computer program development.

An interesting discussion for the student who has difficulty attacking the early stages of problems is in György Pólya's book, *How to Solve It* (2nd ed.; Garden City, N. Y.: Doubleday). The solving of problems is never routine for complex problems, but there are strategies which are often profitable to use. Pólya discusses general tactics that are useful in problem solving.

The second stage in computer program writing begins after the problem is stated as a mathematical problem. We now have to work out the details of the solution to the problem. Techniques in widely different areas of mathematics may be needed, and it may not be obvious as to which techniques are appropriate or what areas of mathematics are useful. With the problems in this book the techniques for numerical solutions of differential equations are almost always needed. Without some knowledge in this area we would not have been able to make progress; with other problems, very different mathematical techniques might have been essential.

The third stage in solving problems on the computer is the writing of the program. It is usually unwise to enter this stage unless the first steps are well in hand. Beginning students tend to go too quickly to the computer, without giving enough thought to the solution method used. This is a temptation, particularly if the computer facility is easily available, but with the inexperienced person, a prematurely written program is likely to lead to wasted time, since it will probably necessitate writing the program many more times than would have been necessary had the details of the calculation been carefully considered in advance. It may not be possible to decide all details in advance and some numerical experimentation may be essential to develop an effective program.

The general method we have been outlining is called an algorithmic method, which involves problems that have a known method of solution. Most problems currently worked on computers are algorithmic; the computer is used only at the third stage of the development. However, there is considerable promise that the computer may be able to contribute more than a large calculating ability for problems whose *method* of solution is already known. The strategy for solving problems where the method of solution is uncertain is called heuristic programming. There are interesting possibilities of using the computer to help with mathematical formulation and choice of mathematical method, particularly in time-sharing systems, which allow a rapid back-and-forth flow of information between the person and the computer. However, we will not discuss heuristic programming further, since it is mostly a possibility for the future rather than something that can be done at present.

EFFICIENT PROGRAMS

For any desired calculation there are a large number of possible programs. All of these are equivalent in the sense that they carry out the desired calculation. But the amount of computer time needed to execute the program may differ from one program to another. Ideally, one would like to use the program taking the least computer time, i.e., the most efficient program. If the program is used only a few times, or if computer time is not scarce, it may not be important to have the optimal program. But for a production program, which will be used over and over again, or for very long programs, optimization may be important. Some recent FORTRAN compilers attempt to optimize the machine language program, but usually this is the responsibility of the programmer. FORTRAN programs are often less efficient than machine language programs.

We have made some attempts at optimization already. For example, in the one-body gravitational problem in Chapter 4 the quantity F was calculated before either force component because it would have been wasteful to calculate this complex expression twice. And in the three-body problem we saved calculational time by computing r^3 immediately rather than r. We could also shorten the harmonic oscillator program by using the initial position and velocity directly in the calculation of velocity for the first half-step.

Generally, optimization is not this simple, and may depend on a working knowledge of the compiler. Here are two examples. Most FORTRAN compilers would accept either of the following statements, and the results would be calculationally equivalent:

$$T = 0$$

$$T = 0.$$

But the second statement will usually execute faster, because the first will require the use of a system-supplied subprogram to convert the fixed-point zero into the floating-point value needed for T. The time-difference may be nontrivial if this statement occurs in a loop which is executed many times, so the decimal point is worth while.

For a second example consider the following calculationally equivalent statements:

$$Y = X * X$$

$$Y = X ** 2$$

The first is likely to be faster, because exponentiation is usually a more involved process than multiplication. With many compilers exponentiation involves $\log(x)$ and $\exp(x)$ subroutines, which would cause the second statement above to be calculated as $\exp(2\log(x))$. Both of the subroutines involve many instructions. On the other hand, floating-point multiplication generally involves less work; on a computer with floating-point hardware only two or three instructions would be needed. Again the differences are magnified if the statement is in an oft-repeated loop.

The computer manufacturer may have literature on writing efficient programs for his own compiler. But we should not leave these questions of efficiency without remarking that machine efficiency should not be the only goal, or perhaps even the most important. While computer time is valuable, it is not as valuable as the time of a creative individual. Hence our principal aim should be the efficient use of *people* rather than the efficient use of machines.

TROUBLES

One of the greatest surprises to the beginning programmer is that, more likely than not, his carefully written program refuses to run! Most texts on computers and programming do not stress this, so it often comes as a surprise; and it is a painful surprise, likely to be repeated many times. It is perhaps comforting to know that it is not solely a problem for the beginner. Almost all computer programs have troubles when they are first written, and do not do what they are expected to do. This is particularly true of complex programs, where it becomes almost impossible to be certain that all possibilities are appropriately taken care of; odd situations can arise that cause unforeseen difficulties, even in programs previously used successfully. Much of the time of computer programmers goes into finding the sources of trouble, a process known as *debugging*. In this section we shall describe the indications of troubles in the program, and in the next section we shall discuss the available resources for eliminating these difficulties.

The first indication of trouble in a FORTRAN program is likely to occur when the program is first compiled. Remember that to use a FORTRAN program it is necessary for the computer to translate the program, using the FORTRAN compiler program, into a machine language program. FORTRAN compilers usually do some checking for grammatical mistakes in a FORTRAN program, since the translation process depends on the proper construction of program statements. If the grammatical rules of FORTRAN are violated by the programmer, there may be ambiguity as to what is intended. FORTRAN compilers must avoid these ambiguities, so they test the structure of each statement, printing error messages when difficulties are encountered. Usually when an error message is printed, compilation stops; however, the compiler may continue to check for certain errors in succeeding statements. Sometimes a compilation is done in several steps, and some errors are not spotted until the second or later pass. In smaller machines error messages may be coded numerically, making it necessary to refer to the FORTRAN manual for that computer for the error codes. In larger machines with more ample storage the error messages are usually in English; however, it may still be necessary to resort to the manual.

It is often necessary to run a program through the compiler several times, correcting the program after each compilation, before you obtain a program that compiles successfully. The amount of error checking varies greatly from compiler to compiler, so the fact that no error messages are obtained is not a positive assurance that your program does not have grammatical mistakes. It is useful to study the FORTRAN manual for the particular system to see just what kinds of errors are found by your compiler.

Once a FORTRAN program has been successfully compiled, the generated machine-language program can be executed. With most FORTRAN systems error messages may also appear when the program is run. Some may be indications of serious trouble. For example, an attempt to divide by zero or an attempt to take the square root of a negative number will usually lead to error messages. When this happens, it usually means that your program is doing something that you do not want it to do. Because the computer has a fixed way of handling numbers, numbers that are too large or too small for its storage methods may occur. These situations are known as *overflow* or *underflow*, and will likely produce error messages.

With large machines some such messages may terminate the program, but with some machines the operator must intervene to stop the calculation. Sometimes the calculation may continue, but the error message will alert you for a possible trouble. Many systems, on being asked to calculate the square root of a negative number, will type an error message, change the sign, and continue the calculation.

Another error in executing a program is more difficult to spot. A FORTRAN program, as every computer program, may contain loops where a set of instructions is used over and over. One way of constructing loops in FORTRAN is with IF statements. It may happen, because of programming mistakes, that the arithmetic expression in the parentheses in the IF never changes sign. So whenever the statement is encountered, the program always goes back to the same statement and comes through to the IF statement again. Such a condition is called an uncontrolled loop. Again, a program in this situation is not doing what it is intended to do; it is also wasting computer time, which is valuable both financially and for the other users' programs. With small machines time may not be a major problem, but with large machines charges are hundreds of dollars an hour. One common procedure in computer centers is to request the person submitting the program to specify a maximum time the program is to run. If the program is not finished at the end of this period, it is removed from the machine, either by the supervisor program or by the operator. This is a protection both for the user, who may have to pay abnormally high charges otherwise, and for the other waiting users of the computer.

Uncontrolled looping is difficult to establish in some situations, since the correct execution of the program may involve going thousands of times through certain loops. Hence it may not be clear whether a loop is a long desired loop or whether there is "no exit." When we discuss trouble correction in the next section, we shall suggest possible methods to distinguish between these two situations.

But by far the most insidious, and perhaps the most common, troubles occur where the program appears to work, prints no error messages, and gives results, i.e., situations where there are no obvious signs of difficulty. We begin with a problem, and pass through stages of a mathematical formulation and a mathematical technique for solving the problem. The critical question that confronts us, and which can never be ignored in computer work, is "Are we working the problem that we think we are working?" In the early days of computer usage it was not realized how easy it is, even for the experienced programmer, to write a program which is *not* doing what the programmer or the problem poser intended it to do. A few early papers published on the basis of computer results later turned out to be "garbage." Most programs are complicated, so the chances for error within the program are greater than the beginning programmer suspects. Furthermore, mathematical techniques are complex, so difficulties may arise before the programming stage is reached.

If this difficulty is so insidious, how can we protect ourselves? There are many ways. Part of the skill of programming is sharpening an intuitive feeling to detect when such things are happening. Perhaps the most generally useful of all the ways of finding hidden difficulties is a special case of a "general principle" which John A. Wheeler at Princeton is fond of giving to physics classes. In *Space-Time Physics*, by E. F. Taylor and J. A. Wheeler (San Francisco: Freeman, 1966), it is called Wheeler's First Moral Principle. It states:

NEVER MAKE A CALCULATION UNTIL YOU KNOW THE ANSWER.

Upon some reflection this seemingly paradoxical principle will be seen to have many applications in solving problems which are beyond our present concern. However, with computers it is indispensable. The first interpretation, which Wheeler stresses, is the importance of *guessing* at an answer before attempting the solution. The person solving a numerical problem, by hand methods or by the computer, should have some idea of the answer; you should be able to see with no calculation at all if the result is going to be around 10^{40} or 10^{-40}, and in many situations a much better guess is possible. Guessing is an important factor in all aspects of problem solving, as Pólya's book, *How to Solve It*, indicates. But it is especially critical in giving some feeling as to where one is going with the problem. Unfortunately, the view of physics as an exact science, and the feeling that it is improper to guess at the answer, is often instilled at the high-school or even elementary-school level, so the student needs to be actively encouraged to guess.

We want to twist Wheeler's First Moral Principle to give it a slightly different meaning. An order-of-magnitude guess may not be good enough to tell us whether the numbers generated by the computer are the desired solution to the problem. The best, and sometimes the only, method for being certain of this is to make some hand calculations and compare these with the computer results. Contrary to popular belief, the computer does *not* relieve the problem solver of the necessity of calculations; because of the possibility of generating large amounts of computer "garbage," hand calculation is important in careful computer usage. At least a few cases should be calculated by a person to ensure that the computer solutions are going in the direction desired. It is not necessary to achieve computer accuracy. How refined a calculation needs to be made—how many significant figures need to be kept—cannot be stated generally, since it depends on the problem. A power of ten calculation may be sufficient, or a slide rule calculation may be needed. Sometimes it is best to use a different method than that used in the computer program, giving the checking procedure a greater degree of accuracy. Just which cases should be checked by hand may require a little reflection; usually they are chosen to make the calculation as easy as possible, although there is the danger that too particular a case may not give an adequate test.

Although the making of calculations is often the only method for determining whether a program is fulfilling its intended purpose, in special situations other methods may be available. One problem in this text suggested one such method.

The problem asked how the three-body problem could be checked. How do we know that the program is carrying out the desired gravitational solution? A hand calculation is difficult because of the amount of calculation involved; hence one wonders if another method might be applicable. In this situation we have already seen a similar but simpler problem, Feynman's calculation for the motion of a single body under an inverse square force which is always directed to a fixed-force center. A little reflection shows that the three-body problem can be made to look very much like the one-body problem. We put one of the bodies very far off initially, so that its force is negligible, and we make a second body very massive and place it initially as the origin with zero velocity; then the remaining body can be started with Feynman's initial conditions. We expect that the values we get will not be too different from the values which Feynman obtains. (Consideration of the choice of masses is left to the student.) Thus we can check our three-body program by simulating a problem with a known result.

That the three-body problem is sometimes effectively a one-body problem is a fortuitous physical accident. In many situations there would not be a previously worked problem for comparison. But perhaps a simpler problem can be constructed to check the original complex problem. Then our checking process has two stages; two programs, the one we want to solve, and a simpler one which is a special case of the first, are written, and the simpler one is checked by hand calculation. The more complex program can then be checked by the simpler program.

DEBUGGING

Although debugging a program to discover why it is not working properly and then making it work properly is one of the most common activities of computer users, there is surprisingly little discussion about debugging, perhaps because the whole business is still very much an art. It is difficult to give any general rules for discovering errors in the program. But certain techniques, while not universally applicable, are usable in a variety of situations.

First, if explicit error messages are available, either during compilation of the FORTRAN program or during execution, the first order of business is to pay attention to these messages. Their meaning is not necessarily obvious. For example, suppose that a beginning programmer intends to indicate the product of two variables A and B. He might, because of his previous use of algebra, forget to use the asterisk for multiplication, and write AB. As far as the FORTRAN compiler is concerned, however, AB is an acceptable variable. Some compilers might note that there was trouble if this variable were on the right-hand side of the calculation without having ever been entered either as data or calculated previously. But the error message would not *say* that a multiplication sign had been left out, for the compiler could not know that you had intended to multiply. Thus an error message is not necessarily obvious; often one feels that the system is making a mistake in the error message. But careful study usually reveals the source of the error. If nothing else, these messages point to the troublesome statement when the error occurs during compilation.

Next we shall discuss a technique useful both for debugging and for writing programs. Several problems have suggested this method, the construction of a flow chart or diagram showing the logical flow of steps in the program. A flow diagram for a given program can be of various degrees of detail; it can closely follow the program, showing explicitly each statement, or it can be a very general formulation of the programmer's intention as to how he wants to solve the problem. The flow chart shown in Fig. 8–1 shows the general structure of the FORCE subroutine discussed earlier. The steps can be described with FORTRAN or with English. There are conventions on symbol shapes in flow charts, but these are not critical.

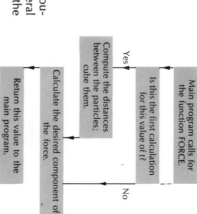

Fig. 8–1. Flow chart for the FORCE subroutine. This particular chart shows the general structure of the subroutine rather than the details.

The most important aspect of a flow diagram is the structure of the branching statements, the statements which alter the sequence and set up loops. If a program has many different branches and loops, it may be very difficult to keep in mind all the possibilities; hence errors become likely in writing the program. However, a visual presentation of the flow of instructions in a flow chart will often show the difficulties in a complex structure. It is almost always advisable to make a flow diagram as the program itself is modified.

Some sophisticated systems with a plotted or cathode-ray tube output can draw flow diagrams directly from a user's program. Such a flow diagram is particularly useful, because it is based not on the intentions of the programmer but rather on the actual program. Where there are errors involved, the intentions and the program may well be two different things, so the machine-constructed flow diagram can be a very helpful debugging aid. As visual terminals become more common in

Main program calls for the function FORCE.

Is this the first calculation for this value of *t*?

Yes

No

Compute the distances between the particles; cube them.

Calculate the desired component of the force.

Return this value to the main program.

computers, it is possible that such facilities will also become more common. Some experimental programming languages have used flow diagrams as the basic program, but this is not possible with FORTRAN.

One technique that is often useful in discovering programming errors is called tracing or running the program in trace mode. Normally, the only printed output is that specified in the program, i.e., the desired information. But many other values may be calculated and these intermediate values are often a clue to difficulties. One troubleshooting possibility is to ask the system to print the result of each calculation; every time an equals sign occurs the value of the expression calculated is printed. In many systems there is a built-in procedure which traces the FORTRAN program, using the sense switches on the console of the computer or control cards preceding the program. But in any case, FORTRAN commands can be inserted in the program at appropriate places. With such printout you can follow each stage of the calculation, and by hand calculations see if the stage is doing what you think it should be doing. Although it may be difficult for a person who has not used trace mode to see how this could be of any advantage, it is often a very useful way of spotting errors. Its use must be limited in very large computers, since enormous quantities of information might be printed if some discretion were not used.

A particularly important application of trace mode concerns IF statements rather than FORTRAN arithmetic statements. The IF statement is the common conditional branching statement in FORTRAN; thus, the failure of an IF statement to do what it is intended to do, either because of the statement itself or because of calculations which preceded, is the principal cause of never-ending loops. Hence in a program which is not working it is of particular interest to know the value of the expression in parentheses in the IF statement each time the statement is executed. Again some FORTRAN systems allow one to find this value through a built-in trace mode operation. However, as before, additional statements can be inserted just before the IF statement to print the value of the expression in the statement. Knowing the value, we can see whether the statement is behaving in the expected way; for example, if we expect to get smaller expressions each time through the loop, but on running the trace mode we find the expressions to be larger each time, then obviously something is wrong in this area of the program. If there are many IF statements in a program and one wants to follow all the branching, it might be useful to insert identifying numbers which would be printed with the values for each of the IF statements.

The decision to run in trace mode must often be made before the computer begins the calculation, both with built-in tracing and with tracing by additional commands. But since it is often desirable to know what is happening and what values the variables have *when the trouble occurs*, it is not surprising that a number of ways exist for doing this. In the FORTRAN program a variable name is a combination of letters and numbers. But during compilation a variable is assigned a location in memory. The programmer may be interested in knowing this location if the program has problems; he may want the values of some of the variables.

The actual process is machine-dependent. With smaller machines, where the programmer is allowed to run the machine, he can stop the program when troubles occur and, using machine language or the console facilities, ask for the contents of the positions in the machine memory. To do this, he must already know what variables are stored where. He can do this if he has obtained during the compilation stage a storage map or symbol table listing the location of variables in the memory. Most FORTRAN compilers generate on request a storage map immediately after compilation; if troubles are likely, a symbol table should be requested. Then, knowing where a variable is stored, an operator of a small machine asks for it with a machine language command. Note that in cases like this FORTRAN debugging forces one to learn a small amount of machine language. The detailed procedures are naturally highly machine-dependent.

With larger and more expensive computers, it is usually out of the question for the writer of a program to enter individual machine language instructions, but related features are available. One can often request a memory "dump" at the time the program is pushed off the machine because of troubles. Such a dump prints the values of all the variables in the program at that time, and perhaps the status of registers and indicators within the computer. Thus it serves some of the purposes of the interrogation that is possible with small machines.

It must be admitted that with both large and small machines the facilities presently available with FORTRAN for finding out what is happening when troubles occur are relatively crude. However, as newer languages are developed, particularly for time-sharing systems, more and more attention is being given to this problem. "Conversational" languages, such as JOSS and BASIC, allow a much more interactive debugging, almost a conversation between the person inserting the program and the computer. But,unfortunately,, at the moment there are few such systems available.

Since it follows that the debugging of a simple program is likely to be easier than the debugging of a complex program, it is a common procedure—almost an essential procedure—to write long programs as a series of shorter programs. Then each shorter program can be checked separately before they are combined to form the full program. Thus if you are writing an involved program, you should write it so that it can be considered as a collection of independent units.

FORTRAN provides one standard mechanism for subdividing programs, and that is the use of subroutines, such as the one we used in our three-body problem.

Although we did not suggest it then, it is possible to run the force program by calling it through a very simple main program which gives values for the variables and requests printout of the calculated force. Using simple input data so that the result could be compared with a hand calculation, this program would check the force subroutine, thus assuring us that the force program would perform its intended task when used as a part of a bigger program. Similarly, the main program for the three-body problem might have been tested by using it with another force subroutine, i.e., a simple force for which the result is obvious. For example, if the function subprogram defines a constant force, then the main program should show that the particle is moving with constant acceleration. In this manner the pieces of the program can be individually freed of trouble before they are put together. This does not guard against difficulties in matching the pieces, but it does pinpoint the source of difficulty.

This technique is not limited to FORTRAN, nor to the use of subroutines. Most complex programs in all programming languages are written as a series of smaller programs, and these subprograms are perfected until each runs satisfactorily by itself. In checking the subprograms, it is often necessary to invent data, as was done in the example of the three-body problem. Many different programmers may be involved in writing subprograms for a very large program.

In concluding the discussion about debugging, we emphasize our starting point: Debugging is not a routine process, and in the present state of computer development it is more an art than a science. Experience enables one to do an increasingly better job of discovering where errors occur.

THE WISE USE OF COMPUTERS

We will conclude on a note of caution. The tendency of the novice computer user is to use the machine constantly; the computer is exciting. A few students lose control; they cannot help playing with the computer as a toy, to the detriment of their other studies. Although this is not common, the student and the instructor should guard against it. The computer is *not* a panacea for all problems. It has definite uses, but in many situations it is of little use or even a positive hindrance. The computer will certainly not replace analytical techniques in physics, and it seems almost certain that analytical techniques will continue to be the bread-and-butter mathematics of the frontier of physics in the foreseeable future.

Each student needs an increasing realization of when the computer can be useful to him and when not. The computer is sometimes referred to as an intelligence amplifier, allowing man to do more with his intelligence than he could do without its aid. But it can also be a stupidity amplifier, particularly if one goes to it prematurely before he has thought out what to do. Since the computer is a new tool in our society, having been used only a few years, the question of where to use it intelligently is difficult, but we must be aware of the question. As more sophisticated computer systems develop and involve more intimate interplay of man and computer, the best attributes of both the man and the computer must be carefully complemented. We end with Norbert Wiener's advice in *God and Golem, Inc.,* one of his last books. He says:

"Render unto man the things which are man's and unto the computer the things which are the computer's. This would seem to be the intelligent policy to adopt when we employ men and computers together in common undertaking. It is a policy as far removed from that of the gadget worshipper as it is from the man who sees only blasphemy and degradation of man in the use of any mechanic adjuvants whatever to thought."*

*Reprinted from *God and Golem, Inc.* by Norbert Wiener by permission of The M.I.T. Press, Cambridge, Massachusetts.

REFERENCES

FORTRAN language guides

There are many published books concerning FORTRAN; we list only a few. For any particular FORTRAN the only final resource is the associated manual, supplied by the computer manufacturer or the compiler writer. Since these manuals change rapidly, and since there are so many, no attempt is made to enumerate them. Computer manufacturers are usually willing to supply manuals on request. The following are a few introductory works on FORTRAN:

FORTRAN in the Physical Sciences. New York: IBM, 1965, Form C20-6634-0.

General Information Manual—FORTRAN. New York: IBM, 1961, Form 28F-8074.

McCRACKEN, D. D., *A Guide to FORTRAN Programming.* New York: John Wiley, 1961.

ORGANICK, E. I., *A FORTRAN Primer.* Reading, Mass.: Addison-Wesley, 1963.

Several recent books concern the extended version of FORTRAN, FORTRAN IV. Among these are the following:

McCRACKEN, D. D., *A Guide to FORTRAN IV Programming.* New York: John Wiley, 1966.

ORGANICK, E. I., *A FORTRAN IV Primer.* Reading, Mass.: Addison-Wesley, 1966.

There are also books which describe FORTRAN and other programming languages for particular computers:

GERMAIN, C. B., *Programming the IBM 1620.* Englewood Cliffs, N. J.: Prentice-Hall, 1962.

References to numerical methods and FORTRAN

An interesting recent development combines a discussion of FORTRAN with a study of numerical methods, exploiting FORTRAN in numerical examples. The first has been written primarily for high-school students while the others are for college and advanced use.

Algorithms, Computation, and Mathematics, revised edition, with supplementary texts on FORTRAN and ALGOL. New Haven: School Mathematics Study Group, 1966.

KUO, S. S., *Numerical Methods in Computers.* Reading, Mass.: Addison-Wesley, 1965.

McCORMICK, J. M., and H. G. SALVADORI, *Numerical Methods in FORTRAN.* Englewood Cliffs, N. J.: Prentice-Hall, 1964.

McCRACKEN, D. D., and W. S. DORNE, *Numerical Methods and FORTRAN Programming.* New York: John Wiley, 1964.

PENNINGTON, R. H., *Introductory Computer Methods and Numerical Analysis.* New York: Macmillan, 1965.

PRAGER, W., *Introduction to Basic FORTRAN Programming and Numerical Methods.* New York: Blaisdell, 1965.

80

Numerical analysis references

There is a large body of literature on numerical methods. While many of the methods which predate computers are still applicable, it is sometimes not clear which is the best method to use for a digital computer, so we list a few recent numerical analysis books that discuss methods that are compatible with computers.

CALINGAERT, P., *Principles of Computation.* Reading, Mass.: Addison-Wesley, 1965.

FOX, L., *Numerical Solution of Ordinary Differential Equations.* Reading, Mass.: Addison-Wesley, 1963.

FRÖBERG, C. E., *Introduction to Numerical Analysis.* Reading, Mass.: Addison-Wesley, 1965.

HAMMING, R. W., *Numerical Methods for Scientists and Engineers.* New York: McGraw-Hill, 1962.

HENRICI, P., *Discreet Variable Methods in Ordinary Differential Equations.* New York: John Wiley, 1962.

HENRICI, P., *Elements of Numerical Analysis.* New York: John Wiley, 1964.

NOBLE, B., *Numerical Methods.* Edinburgh: Oliver and Boyd, 1964.

SINGER, J., *Elements of Numerical Analysis.* New York: Academic Press, 1964.

STIEFEL, E. L., *An Introduction to Numerical Mathematics.* New York: Academic Press, 1963.

INDEX

index